# THE
# REDWOODS

By Kramer Adams

POPULAR LIBRARY • NEW YORK

## *About the Author*

Kramer Adams is a fourth-generation native of northern California whose love for the charms of the West has been only thinly concealed in two earlier books and numerous articles in publications such as *American Forests, American Motorist, Argosy, Forest History, Journal of Forestry, Outdoor America,* and *Western Conservation Journal.*

His storytelling talents are now turned to explaining the little-known facts about the redwoods and the most significant conservation battle of our time, that surrounding the establishment of a coast redwood national park.

For credentials, Mr. Adams brings his employment background as public-recreation administrator, newspaperman, editor, and public-relations executive with the California Department of Fish and Game, California Redwood Association, and American Forest Institute. Educated at San Francisco Bay Area colleges and the University of California, he is a former vice president of the Outdoor Writers Association and national committee chairman of the Izaak Walton League. He is a member of the Save-the-Redwoods League, the Forest History Society, and the American Forestry Association.

POPULAR LIBRARY EDITION

# Contents

# Introduction

The Redwood Region, it is called, in honor of what may be the most famous trees on earth. Geographically, it is a foggy strip of the Pacific Coast where *Sequoia sempervirens* ranges for five hundred miles in red and green profusion, growing in predictably irregular groves and forests along the Coast Range. Psychologically, it extends deep into the great conservation guilt complex of America. Politically, it is a battlefield for what has been called the conservation issue of the century. And outside the borders of its favored three thousand square miles, it is, perhaps, largely a state of mind.

According to man's arbitrary political designations, the region sprawls across fifteen counties, centering near San Francisco and embracing the nine ocean-side counties from central California's Monterey on the south through Curry County, Oregon, on the north. Inland, the redwood counties include the mellifluous heritage of Spanish- and Indian-named San Benito, Santa Clara, Contra Costa, Alameda, Lake, and Napa.

In common with most Californians, the redwood is a newcomer, another refugee from colder climes. It has settled down after millions of years of world-wandering and by adaptation and mutation, developed into a most strange and beautiful plant.

Yet you feel that the great trees must always have been there, as their ancestors were when life crawled out of the slime to evolve into man.

Looking upward to the lacy green ceiling, the thoughtful visitor in the old redwood forest melds into a silent partnership of light, water, earth, and trees.

The towering red-barked aspiration seems endless. As a mysterious half-light echoes among the trees, human senses are humbled.

The big Sequoias are not looked at, they are experienced.

This is the familiar world of the picture-postcard redwood,

the cathedral groves admired by tourists, the forest most worthy of man's protection. But there are other redwood worlds to be known if the forest pilgrim would do more than look mutely upon the trees; if he is to involve himself in the public policies that will assure the redwood adventure for his children and theirs, and if he would heighten his own experience with knowledge.

From the time redwood became one of the most useful plants on earth, there was bound to be conflict over its conversion to man's needs. This is a mystical tree, inspiring the emotions like no other. As the focus of worldwide attention and concern in the recent campaign for a coast redwood national park, the facts about the tree were obscured by exaggeration, surrounding it with a false folklore as thick as its bark. Paul Bunyan himself could have dreamed up tales no fancier than those now cherished and firmly believed across the land.

The tree is not, as described by the President of the United States in a 1968 speech, the oldest known. It is not the largest of all trees, as *Life* magazine claims. It is not the tallest living thing of all time, as the National Park Service reports. It is quite the opposite of the fast-disappearing species mentioned by a recent Secretary of the Interior. Its botanical name does not mean "the tree that never dies," as contended by the principal speaker at the dedication of Redwood National Park. It is not slow-growing, as many believe, but among the fastest. Nor does it grow only in California, as a red-faced governor of Oregon had to be reminded.

Such statements, usually uttered in the well-meaning cause of conservation, serve only to delay our understanding of a complex and fascinating story. Nor are any simplistic counterstatements worthy of the tall Sequoia. Both demonstrate the foolishness of applying our shortcut culture of symbols and semantic sophistry—the popular language of nearly all who have spoken or written on the redwoods—to an ancient heritage as yet only partly understood.

The confusion explains, in part, why the redwood has been called the most widely publicized but least known tree on the planet.

In the attempt to chop a trail through the thicket of misunderstanding, this book will deal only with the redwood species that has become the center of attention and, except for an early description of their differences, will ignore the giant redwood of the Sierra and the dawn redwood of China.

To qualify as a tree-watcher, one must know that the term "board foot," used by lumbermen and park rangers alike, means the equivalent of a one-inch-thick piece of wood twelve inches square. The value of this platter-sized slice—in a standing tree and untouched—ranges from five cents to thirty cents or more. A single tree may be worth thousands of dollars.

There will be understandable resentment caused by this tampering with the forest fairy tales and the reduction of the mighty redwood—even though it be only by words—into board feet and dollar signs. Yet for two centuries, the history of the tree has been essentially an economic history, embracing the frustrations of the preservationists as well as the callousness of the highball loggers. The remarkable redwood is, stripped of sentiment, the earth's largest plant with an economic value.

It is one of the best building materials known. About two thirds of this year's production of a quarter billion dollars' worth of redwood products will go across the nation and overseas as a prime symbol of the envied good life of California, its materialistic, affluent, leisurely, and tasteful ways.

This worldwide market supports the economy of a large section of California. Redwood is a livelihood for twenty thousand workers.

They are clerks, pulp mill technicians, foresters, railroad engineers, loggers, salesmen, scientists, and mill hands. Among their predecessors in the redwood pageant were such colorful figures as Captain John Sutter, Bret Harte, Thomas Larkin, and General Vallejo; Russian, Spanish and Mexican colonists; a San Francisco scoundrel named Harry Meiggs; Kit Carson, John Muir, and President Grant.

In their larger-than-life setting, the people of the redwoods seem to stand a little taller, clinging to a frontier ethic tempered by past challenges met and conquered.

Some of the forty redwood products companies they work for have been in business for a hundred years and most have made costly investments in the future. Since 1960, these firms have spent more than $100 million in new plants, equipment, and improvements. And in the next ten years, capital investments in new mills for producing redwood plywood, pulp, paper, and particle board will add up to another $100 million.

This trend suggests some disagreement with the frequent warning that we are running out of redwoods, that the timber products economy is declining. Admirers of the tree should be interested in learning why the 100,000 owners and shareholders of these companies are willing to bet differently.

Aldo Leopold called conservation the ability of man to live in harmony with the land. There is now no reason to doubt that the considerable social and product benefits of the redwood, to a degree greater than most other renewable natural resources, can be maintained indefinitely with proper management and that these two redwood worlds, at least, can continue in harmony.

There is less encouragement to be found when we examine the tree's ecological world. Here, all clues lead to the shocking realization that the best of the redwoods—those we presumed were protected in parks—may ultimately be doomed to extinction. Though the end will not come in our time, the process is being hastened by both man and nature, and the informed observer can see the first tragic symptoms now in the great lowland groves. How long we can keep the redwood alive on a hostile planet will depend largely on an enlightened public.

There's heartwarming evidence of this magic tree's ability to inspire humans to be found in the generous donations of land and money that have helped make the public the largest of all landowners in the redwoods and encouraged a cooperative program of tree preservation without precedent in world history.

You'll find no Paul Bunyan stories about the redwoods, though other genre of tall tales about the tall trees are not hard to find. In the many worlds of the Sequoia, the superlative is the commonplace. This is a tree that makes its own legends.

California's foremost botanist, the late Willis L. Jepson, wrote in 1928 that "we know little about our wonderful tree. We know less about the redwood belt of ancient geologic times which is the real key to an understanding of many other things about our California that we cannot as yet fully anticipate."

Since Jepson's words of forty years ago, much has been learned about the strange gathering of giants—hard-won scraps of information that can be helpful in our attempts to keep the species alive and productive.

On the 200th anniversary of modern man's discovery of the coast redwood, it is of urgent timeliness to pause and consider this gift of eternity.

# Chapter I

## *The Three Redwoods*

The name of the first literate man to look upon the redwoods may never be known. It could have been the bold Chinese explorer Hui Shan, who sailed the Pacific rim in A.D. 458 and mentioned American forests having "tall trees of red wood."

It may have been Captain Juan Rodríguez Cabrillo who, in 1542, looked landward and called Alta California's wooded shore "the coast of pines." Later in the century, Captains Francis Drake and Sebastián Cermeno both landed in the heart of the Redwood Region.

Perhaps these adventurers found their surroundings so wondrous that the unusual red trees were not worth mentioning. If any spoke up, his comments have since become a secret of the forests.

The revelation waited until Spanish colonists established their mission near Monterey. From this most northerly outpost of western America, Don Gaspar de Portolá and a small party headed overland to the north on an exploratory trip that would result in the discovery of San Franciso Bay.

As they approached the Santa Cruz Mountains, northeast of today's Watsonville, the party's chaplain and official diarist commented on "the very high trees of a red color, not known to us." On October 10, 1769, Brother Juan Crespi became the discoverer of the coast redwoods when he wrote, "In this region there is a great abundance of these trees and because none of the expedition recognizes them, they are named *palo colorado*, from their color."

9

The redwoods had been around for a million centuries. Leaf imprints in ancient coal and rock formations show the Northern Hemisphere alone has known nearly fifty different species. About a dozen redwoods were native to North America in the age of the dinosaurs, and of these, three have adapted to harsh climatic and environmental changes of the millenniums and survive today.

Members of the so-called redwood family, Taxodiaceae, are still primitive plants. Scaly leafed, each tree grows inconspicuous male and female flower buds on different branches. The woody, egg-shaped cones produce deceptively small seeds, which, like those of Jack's beanstalk, offer no hint of their potential.

It is still a large family with ten genera and sixteen species scattered over the earth. But only three species are commonly called redwood.

Until Brother Crespi's redwood of coastal California and Oregon was botanically classified it had many names. The pioneering Spaniards labeled it red pine, *madera colorada de California*, alerche, spruce, and sabino. In the nineteenth century, lumbermen gave it such names as red tree, Humboldt redwood, California cedar, cypress, redwood cedar, and bastard cedar.

The first botanical collection of the coast redwood was probably made by Thaddeus Haenke, exploring California with the Malaspena expedition of 1791. But the scientist generally credited with the discovery is Scotsman Archibald Menzies. In 1794 he visited Santa Cruz with the Vancouver expedition and sent seeds, cones, and olive-green foliage back to the Natural History Museum in London, where they are still on display.

The strange new tree was unbaptized until 1823. British botanist A. B. Lambert then assumed it was of the same genus as the bald cypress and called it the evergreen Taxodium. Not until 1847 did the Austrian Stephan Endlicher discover the error. While the coast redwood was entitled to be called sempervirens—evergreen—it was not a Taxodium. He established a new genus, Sequoia.

Endlicher's choice of a name was unusual but appropriate. Sequoya was the name of a Cherokee Indian chief who never saw a redwood. He served the United States as a soldier in the War of 1812 and acquired the official name of George Guess, a surname that may have been given in an unkind reference to his white father and Indian mother.

Time has proved Sequoya to be a red man worthy of patronizing the great red trees, his principal achievement being the creation of a Cherokee alphabet that brought enlightenment to his people and encouragement to other tribes.

*Chief Sequoya, whose Latinized name was given to the redwoods, was an unschooled cripple who spent twelve years developing an alphabet for his Cherokee Indians. The tribe was able to translate the Bible and other works and collectively bought a press for printing their own newspaper.*

The redwood of the Coast Range was now officially *Sequoia sempervirens*. It had been discovered by a Spaniard, collected by a Scotsman, and named by an Austrian to honor an American Indian.

The tree has been traced back to the Cretaceous period of one hundred million years ago, becoming common throughout the Northern Hemisphere during the early part of the Tertiary period, sixty million years ago. Fossils bearing its flat, sharp-pointed needles have been unearthed in Texas and Pennsylvania. Yellowstone National Park has a standing petrified redwood with a twenty-eight-foot-thick trunk.

By the Pleistocene epoch of one or two million years ago, great sheets of advancing glacial ice had pushed the tree out of Japan, the Himalayas, and western Europe, restricting it to western North America.

Across the great valley of central California and about one hundred miles east of the nearest sempervirens, another evergreen redwood was taking refuge from time in the snow-topped mountains of the Sierra Nevada.

"In the last two days travelling we have found some trees of 16 to 18 fathoms [96 to 108 feet] around the trunk," wrote Zenas Leonard of Captain Joseph R. Walker's expedition in 1833. The fifty-man party was on its way from Nevada to California, and passing through a portion of what is now Yosemite National Park, its members became the first white men to see the giant redwoods.

The big tree called "wawona" by the Mokelumne tribe is the most massive plant species on earth. Looking at its great stem, one can understand why the Indians honored it with godlike qualities and drank its purple sap in the hope of acquiring some mystic power. Tall, with a gracefully tapering trunk that illusions into infinity, the Big Tree grows far-spaced in the open, parklike forest common to the western Sierra.

Soon after the Gold Rush, the Chelsea (London) nursery firm of James Veitch dispatched Professor William Lobb to California to collect plant specimens suitable for decorating British gardens. In 1852, he sent back seeds, the blue-green foliage, and a description of the Big Tree that permitted botanist John Lindley to record its botanical debut. The new find was named *Wellingtonia gigantea* in honor of the Duke of Wellington, hero of Waterloo, who had died a year earlier.

There seems to be something about the redwoods that inspires disagreements. French botanist Joseph Decaisne decided that while the tree was a new species all right, it was in the same genus as the coast redwood. In 1854, he named it *Sequoia gigantea*. Soon after, a patriotic Yankee botanist tried to establish the name *Americus gigantea*. The U.S. Forest Service ignored them all and officially used *Sequoia washingtonia* for many years.

The botanical laws of precedent were to prevail. Though the layman calls it Big Tree, Sequoia, Sierra redwood, mammoth tree, and giant redwood, the scientific world—except for England—stuck with *Sequoia gigantea*.

Until 1939, anyway. Dr. J. T. Buchholtz of the University of Illinois then discovered that the chromosome numbers of the coast and Sierra species were different. Different enough, he claimed, to justify a new genus to be called *Sequoiadendron giganteum*. Most of the scientific community concurs and there is a movement to make the change official as soon as possible. It would take some time, however, to get used to a renamed Sequoiadendron National Park.

Not so fast, say the tradition-conscious British botanists who have been using *Wellingtonia gigantea* all along. If it is a separate genus, as Lindley claimed more than a hundred years ago, then his original designation of Wellingtonia should be honored. To climax a century of confusion it is possible the Big Tree's new name may be the old one after all.

Less is known about the history of the Sierra redwood than the coastal species, but fossils tested by radiology show that it, too, had its origin in the Cretaceous period. It had occurred in Europe, Greenland, and throughout North America about sixty thousand centuries in the past.

There are striking similarities in the two California redwoods, though writer Bret Harte termed sempervirens "a poor cousin" of the family. Both are relatively fire-resistant, free of insects and disease, thick-barked, and fast-growing. But the coarse, splintery wood of the Sierra species has little value, and commercial logging ended long ago. The Big Tree lives much longer, to 3,200 years. And it grows twice as large, the General Sherman weighing in at an incredible 2.5 million pounds.

Most commentators agree with Harte that the Big Tree is the more majestic, awe-inspiring, and graceful of the two trees—indeed, of all trees.

As early as 1864, it was recognized that this natural wonder should be available for all to enjoy. In that year, President Abraham Lincoln signed the act transferring Yosemite Valley and the Mariposa Big Tree Grove to the State of California. This created the first of the nation's state parks. In 1890, the land was deeded back to the federal government to become the nucleus of today's Yosemite National Park.

Other Sierra groves were added to state and federal reservations over the years until at the end of the last century, botanist William R. Dudley of Stanford University was able to call *Sequoia gigantea* "the best-protected species of tree in the New World." The thirty-six thousand acres of Sierra redwood in government reserves today, according to consulting foresters Frank and Dean Solinsky, represent ninety-nine percent of all the natural trees in existence.

So important have the two native Sequoias been in the

state's cultural history that the legislature had little choice in designating them jointly as California's official tree.

Throughout most of modern scientific history, the two red trees were considered to be the only living survivors of the many redwoods of the past. Then came the recent discovery of a third redwood, and with it a landmark adventure in science.

Fossilized leaves of a primitive tree now called the dawn redwood had been found since the middle of the last century in northern Asia, Greenland, and western North America in rocks laid down during the last one hundred million years. Because of their similarities, this redwood relic was assigned to the same genus as bald cypress and the two living redwoods.

Only months before the attack on Pearl Harbor, paleobotanist Shigeru Miki had been collecting fossils near Kobe, Japan, and came across a redwood specimen that showed distinct differences from the known types. Rather than the alternating needles found on twigs of the coast redwood, it had needles that grew in linear precision opposite each other. Miki also found differences in the olive-sized cones, which had long, naked stalks. He assigned it a new genus, Metasequoia, meaning newest or successive Sequoia.

The revelation meant that many of the world's redwood fossils believed to have been variations of sempervirens or gigantea would have to be relabeled.

While wars raged, a forester employed by the Chinese government in 1944 stumbled upon a large, unfamiliar tree growing in a remote section of Central China near the village of Mo-tao-chi. Investigating further, Tsang Wang found more of the trees, called water pines, growing along the river valley. He took leaf and cone samples back to civilization.

The tree was identified at Nanking's National Central University as the long-lost Metasequoia. News of the discovery excited the scientific world and postwar plans were made to study this mysterious link to the past in its natural habitat. But time was short. Civil war divided China. Communist armies advanced toward the valley of Shui-haa and further investigation was threatened. Meanwhile, Tsang reported, the natives continued their practice of chopping down the rare trees for the building of cabinets.

Just ahead of the Bamboo Curtain, Dr. Ralph W. Chaney, professor of paleobotany at the University of California, trekked to the remote spot on an expedition financed by the Save-the-Redwoods League. And botanist Tsang flew into the valley on a last-minute collecting trip sponsored by Harvard University's Arnold Arboretum.

Dr. Chaney found only a thousand living specimens. Many tapered skyward more than one hundred feet, and some were

**SEMPERVIRENS       GIGANTEA       DAWN**

estimated to be three hundred years old. Thin-barked, their trunk diameters ranged from 6½ to 9½ feet at the base.

Just a few weeks behind the scientists, Red soldiers closed off the valley. Metasequoia had been exposed briefly only to be thrust again into its mysterious past and scientific limbo.

But the two scientists had done their job well. They had recorded important basic information. And despite government bans, Dr. Chaney and Tsang managed to bring out seeds and cuttings that were distributed to nurseries, arboretums, and institutions around the world. These young trees, some now past adolescence, will provide much-needed scientific information over the years.

Surprisingly, the exotic tree is thriving under a variety of conditions. In the United States it is common enough now to be found in commercial nurseries. It gains popularity as a decorative specimen and a home-garden conversation piece.

In common with the traits that have permitted the Sierra and coast redwoods to survive the centuries, *Metasequoia*

**SEMPERVIRENS**          **GIGANTEA**

**DAWN**

*glyptostroboides* has been found to be fast-growing and resistant to insects and disease. Twenty-year-old trees are now thirty or forty feet tall. Cuttings grow readily. Relatively hardy, the dawn redwood is little affected by weather changes or extremes of temperature, though a family characteristic shows up in its preference for well-drained, moist soil. This strange redwood is deciduous, imitating its relative, the bald cypress of the southeastern United States by shedding its light-green needles each year.

Each of the three redwoods have had long journeys. It seems certain that the migrants made use of the ancient land bridge that connected Asia and the North American continent. St. Lawrence Island, now in the Bering Sea, once bore a dense forest of redwoods. As the subtropical climates of the hemisphere cooled and dried some sixty-five million years ago, the range of the three species began to recede.

Today, the Metasequoia makes its tenuous last stand in a sort of botanical Shangri-la. The Sierra redwood, threatened

## THE THREE REDWOODS

|  | Coast | Sierra | Dawn |
|---|---|---|---|
| OLDEST | 2,200 years | 3,200 years | 300 years |
| TALLEST | H. A. Libbey Tree | California Tree | unnamed |
| HEIGHT | 367 feet | 310 feet | 100 feet (?) |
| LOCATION | Redwood National Park | Kings Canyon National Park | Hupeh, China |
| LARGEST | Stout Tree | General Sherman | unnamed |
| DIAMETER | 20 feet | 32.2 feet | 3.5 feet |
| LOCATION | Jedediah Smith State Park | Sequoia National Park | China |
| CONE SIZE | 1 inch | 2½ inches | ¾ inch |
| NUMBER OF SEEDS | 30 to 60 | 100 to 250 | 50 (?) |
| ELEVATION | 0–3,000 feet | 3,000–8,300 feet | 4,000 feet |

by ecological changes, is barely holding its own in seventy groves scattered from a point west of California's Lake Tahoe south along the Sierra Nevada for 270 miles. Only the sempervirens, far from endangered and once described by a scientist as a million times more numerous than gigantea, now thrives in what may be increasing numbers in its latest home along the Oregon and California coast.

Here the three Sequoias stand, symbols of nature's permanence. How did they—respectively the tallest, largest, and perhaps rarest of living trees—arrive at our doorstep? What wonderful selective process chose them, along with few other plants, to fight their way through the eons to the Age of the Atom?

## Chapter II

## *Where the Fog Flows*

Of all the places where it once lived, the sempervirens has chosen to settle down as part of the wild beauty of the Pacific West.

Out where the Coast Range stands knee-deep in the ocean, a weather effect called the Pacific High delivers warm, moist air from the central Pacific to a rendezvous with cold, southerly air currents of the coast. The meeting produces the soft gray fogs that creep ashore for one fourth of the days of the year. Here, too, rain clouds encounter their first land obstacle and dump their burden on crazy-tilted green mountains. The combination creates redwood country, a favored strip of land where Time has paused for a while.

The coast redwood seizes the moisture and, aided by rich, young soils, spires in shaggy grace to the tallest of surviving plants.

This Sequoia could have settled elsewhere, but competing tree species and its great thirst have cornered it in our time into a five-hundred-mile-long intermittent belt that seldom ventures more than thirty miles from the ocean's moisture. "Where the fog flows, the redwood grows" advises a folk rhyme of the region.

In a climate where it is not unusual on a summer day to drive with car headlights and windshield wipers turned on, residents might understandably console themselves that the bothersome fog does, after all, produce their wonderful redwoods. But the fog flows elsewhere too, and other ele-

18

ments of the scientists' law of limiting factors—soil type and location—must be given equal credit with climate for the phenomenon called sempervirens.

In its precarious southerly ventures, the redwood dwindles out where the amount of rainfall drops below thirty inches a year. The migration ends in wind-protected canyons of the Santa Lucia Mountains, about a dozen miles north of Hearst's San Simeon Castle. Here the stretch between winter rain and summer fog is not quite long enough to bring the dry death called desiccation.

To the east, reduced rainfall and occasional hot winds keep the tree huddled close to the Coast Range. Small groves in San Benito, Napa, and Lake counties and in the hills behind Oakland and Berkeley are the region's easterly outposts.

To the north, scattered groves in the Chetco River area of Oregon's southwestern corner mark the point where frost and winter weather conditions begin to kill off seedlings.

Even on the western oceanfront the range is delimited by tree-killing salt spray, persistent winds, and the general lack of fog and rain adjacent to the beaches.

From one end of the region to the other, rainfall, climate, soils, and topography vary greatly, having only one thing in common—moisture.

Northwestern California residents say it's a dry winter day when it only drizzles, and point to an annual rainfall that averages three or four times more than San Francisco's twenty inches.

The north coast, with ten percent of the state's land area, produces thirty-seven percent of its water. From Santa Cruz County north, the frequent floods called trashmovers are both blessing and curse, but an essential in the redwood's ecological world.

The weather station at Point Reyes, geographical pivot of the region, is the foggiest on the Pacific Coast.

At the ineptly named Honeydew Weather Station, located a few miles west of the Rockefeller Forest, a record California rainfall of 174 inches—14½ feet—has been measured in one year.

Nearly everywhere, the redwoods grow in what appears to be a rain forest, relatively humid and tropiclike, knit together by luxuriant undergrowth. It's not hard to understand why early residents and not a few scientists believed the redwoods were responsible for causing fog and rain by drawing moisture from the air. Extending the theme, the president of the State Horticultural Society in 1874 went so far as to predict the cutting of redwoods would cause California to become a desert.

The tree's unusual ability to make use of moisture in the air to supplement its supply from the ground may account for the coast redwood's abundance in contrast to the scarcity of its two living relatives. It does this by collecting fog on its leaves, then letting the water drip down the trunk or onto the ground where near-surface rootlets can drink. In measured instances, fog drip has accounted for the equivalent of fifty inches a year in rain.

In another way fog helps the redwood by creating a semi-shade from the summer sun, which retards evaporation of the moisture.

Do the old trees signal that they are dying of thirst? Some scientists cautiously suggest this may be true. The naked, gray spike top that appears before a doomed tree topples is proba-bly caused by the inability of the trunk to carry enough water to its top. The distressing sight is common in public parks, where visitor campgrounds, roads, and trails have compacted the soil. Dead crowns are evident also along highways, where asphalt paving robs the wide-ranging roots of water and re-moves needed moisture from the air.

In a country where the climate is mild and nearly snow-free, the redwood—storing more water in its trunk than any other conifer—sometimes makes up for lack of fog and pre-cipitation by utilizing ground water sources. One nearly fog-free grove is found at creekside in Las Posadas State Forest, forty-five air miles east of the ocean.

El Palo Alto, the San Francisco Peninsula's landmark tree named by the Portolá expedition, is a conspicuous loner, standing in grandeur on the bank of San Francisquito Creek. The nearest redwood forest is five miles away, and from this source its seed was probably washed down the creek five hun-dred years ago. In the twentieth century, as the area around Stanford University built up, a series of flood-control dams and diversions was installed. The tree's year-round supply of creekwater dwindled, and the spike top of approaching death appeared. After consultations with foresters, the City of Palo Alto rigged up an ingenious artificial fog system. For one hundred feet, a water pipe runs up the trunk and sends out a

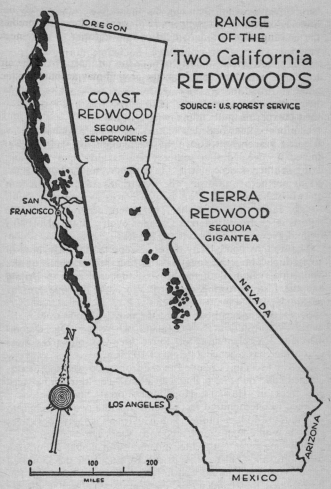

RANGE
OF THE
Two California
REDWOODS
SOURCE: U.S. FOREST SERVICE

OREGON

COAST
REDWOOD
SEQUOIA
SEMPERVIRENS

SAN
FRANCISCO

SIERRA
REDWOOD
SEQUOIA
GIGANTEA

NEVADA

N

LOS ANGELES

ARIZONA

0        100       200
MILES

MEXICO

fine spray during dry periods. The Tall Tree is now out of
danger.

While the coast redwood's natural range is hemmed in by
soil, moisture, and climate conditions, it has proved capable
of taking hold at many other places on the planet. Inspired by
the beauty of the forest, the dimensions of the tree, and its

commercial possibilities, experimenters have been planting seeds and seedlings abroad for more than a century.

The Russians are credited with being the first to bring the redwood out of California alive. Sometime during the first four decades of the nineteenth century, the colonists at Fort Ross sent *Sequoia sempervirens* seeds back to the mother country. From the Czar's nursery, seeds or seedlings found their way to England in the 1840's. The tree has since been planted experimentally in many parts of the world.

California Redwood Association has made a global survey of forestry agencies to learn the whereabouts of planted specimens. It revealed that sempervirens is alive and well and living in thirty-nine countries. Like their young-growth brothers in northern California, the expatriates are adding a foot or two in height each year in such places as England, South Africa, Japan, and Australia. There were generally favorable reports also from Ireland, Canada, Wales, Italy, Northern Ireland, New Zealand, and the U.S.S.R.

The Johnny-come-lately forests seem to do their best in areas duplicating the foggy, damp, but mild climate of the California region. Both the heaviest timbered area in Britain and the fastest-growing coniferous forest in Europe are the redwoods planted in misty Wales.

Sempervirens has been called the most valuable tree in the world by foresters in New Zealand, where it is logged commercially. A plantation of thirty-three-year-old trees near Cambridge has reached a height of 105 feet.

Seeds or seedlings planted in the tropics do well too, it was learned, but only in higher elevations. The thirty-nine-year-old trees in Hawaii's Honaunau Forest plantation have zoomed to one hundred feet in the temperate two-thousand- to six-thousand-foot altitude. South Africa's ninety-foot trees grow on a mile-high site planted forty years ago.

Only one report prevented unanimity in global admiration for California's tall tree. A British forester said the imported sempervirens was doing well in several areas of Scotland. But he revealed that residents in the remote Wye Valley district objected to redwood plantings because they were too tall, had a foreign appearance, and "reduced the amenity value" of the neighborhood.

In many parts of the world, including the United States east of the Rockies, the tree is a poor risk because of temperature extremes and quick changes in climate.

The foreign experimenters have found sempervirens unsuited to some growing sites because it does not have a water-seeking central taproot, as many trees do. It has instead several stubby main roots, never deeper than six feet, fed by a maze of thin, wormlike filaments that rise to one or two feet from the ground surface. This part of the tree's waterworks, always struggling to satisfy the redwood's lifetime need for one thousand tons of water for each ton of its weight, is a continuously dividing network that may circle out as far as one hundred feet from the trunk and sometimes interlocks with roots of neighboring trees. These hairless roots grow horizontally during the winter and sometimes upwards after floods have deposited new silt on the ground.

Another reason for the tree's long life on an unfriendly planet is found in its remarkable ability to regenerate these roots. Chop off either main or feeder roots, and like a lizard's tail or a crab's claw, they soon regrow.

Under its security blanket of fog, the coast redwood has proved to be one of nature's most efficient machines for photosynthesis. This process, by which plants manufacture food through the green chlorophyll of their leaves, requires an abundance of light in other western conifers. But the redwood can grow vigorously where the sunlight is less than one percent of full intensity, according to researcher reports, and does so nearly twice as fast as its nearest competitor. This earns it the description of a shade-tolerant tree.

The recipe for growth calls for carbohydrates, produced when the leaves take sun and carbon dioxide from the air, mixed well with soluble materials that the roots have picked up from the soil. This adds new layers of wood fibers on the outside of the old. As most of the growth takes place in spring and early summer, the fall periods of slow growth are marked by dark, hard lines in the wood. The age of redwood can be determined by counting these annual growth rings on cut stumps, or by means of a hollow boring tool that withdraws a pencil-thin sample of ringed wood between the center and the bark of a living trunk.

The coast redwood, in common with its Sierra cousin, reaches a relatively great age because of its high resistance to three principal enemies of other trees—fire, insects, and fungus disease.

Among the romantic fantasies about the coast redwood is that of its longevity. The tree has been widely touted as the

# HOW A REDWOOD GROWS

CARBON DIOXIDE FROM AIR

MINERALS & WATER FROM SOIL

LIGHT & HEAT FROM SUN

COMBINE IN LEAVES TO PRODUCE

**PLANT FOOD**

**CROWN**
THE FOOD FACTORY
OF THE TREE

ENTIRE TREE BREATHES IN
OXYGEN THROUGH PORES IN
LEAVES, TWIGS, BRANCHES,
TRUNK AND ROOTS

HEARTWOOD - A LIFELESS RIGID
COLUMN SUPPORTING THE TREE

SAPWOOD - LIVING WOOD WHICH
CARRIES WATER & MINERALS UPWARD

CAMBIUM - MICROSCOPIC GROWTH
LAYER WHICH PRODUCES WOOD & BARK

**TRUNK**

INNER BARK - LIVING BARK THAT
DISTRIBUTES FOOD MFD· BY LEAVES

WATER CONTAINING SMALL
AMOUNTS OF MINERALS IS
TAKEN IN BY THE FINEST ROOTS

OUTER BARK - PROTECTIVE COVERING
OF TRUNK, BRANCHES & ROOTS

**ROOTS**

oldest living thing on earth, an opinion shared by, among others, a U.S. senator who sponsored a redwood national park bill. A few school books repeat the old myth.

*Sequoia sempervirens* is the fourth oldest known species of tree in California. It is outlived by the bristlecone pine (*Pinus aristata*), whose oldest specimen carried 4,600 annual rings; the Sierra redwood at a maximum of 3,200 years; and the western juniper (*Juniperus occidentalis*), which reaches an age of 3,000 years.

Elsewhere, according to Harry D. Tiemann of the U.S. Forest Service, specimens of cypress, yew, oak, cedar, blackbutt, baobab, and chestnut have been reported to surpass the oldest coast redwood in age. And several tree species grow larger.

"The public has been given the impression that all redwood trees are immense in size and hoary with age," claims Professor Emeritus Emanuel Fritz of the University of California School of Forestry. "The fact is a tree 1,800 years old or older is a great rarity. The greatest age so far determined by an actual count of the growth rings is just over 2,200."

The conclusion of a half century of sampling and studies shows that less than three percent of the redwoods are over one thousand years old. There are probably none that old to be found in the federally owned section of Redwood National Park, though most writers revert to the cliché that "these trees were young when Christ walked the earth."

Fritz, Dr. Edward C. Stone, the Forest Service, and other authorities agree that the normal life-span of the sempervirens is from five hundred to eight hundred years. Death may come from fire or a lack of moisture. A day comes when, burdened by their great weight, the oldsters lose their balance and fall over, a process that can happen in a windstorm, a flood, or on the calmest summer day.

Size is not a reliable indicator of age. The six-foot-thick trunks of stump sprouts behind Fort Ross are larger at 150 years than most of the old-growth trees found in state parks. Forester D. W. Cooper of the California Agricultural Extension Service reports a longevity study in which the annual growth rings of fifteen hundred stumps were counted, ranging to monsters fifteen feet in diameter. The largest was found to be just over seven hundred years old, the next largest being in the 350- to 600-year class.

The 2,200-year-old tree discovered by Fritz in 1934 had a diameter of twelve feet, but so do some trees only one quarter that age. One redwood at the age of four hundred years measured nineteen inches across. On a single acre, tree diameters may range from less than one foot to ten or twelve feet.

This wide range in size and age, while unusual among trees, is characteristic of the old-growth and virgin redwood forest. It is considered a subclimax type, close to being the ultimate natural development of vegetation able to maintain itself on a given piece of land. A few redwood stands, including those in the National Park's Redwood Creek Valley, consist of trees of about the same age, probably because of forest-killing fires in the past. Outside the even-aged stands of the lowland groves, the forest is a world always in transition, new individual trees replacing the old.

The home of the redwoods includes some of the roughest real estate in California, no more than five percent of it being level. The cliffs that nearly everywhere mark the meeting of the Redwood Region and the Pacific are reminders that there was a great geologic uplift here only half a million years ago. Some inland ridges are of such recent geological formation that they are actually steeper than the angle of repose of the materials of which they are formed.

The result is varied and unstable soil formations. A marine sandstone is the prevailing type, complicated here and there with a later stratum. High in acid, it has a clayey to sandy consistency, greasy when wet, and with a capacity for holding much water. This is to the redwood's liking, for it can live even in gravel as long as there is enough moisture.

In the earthquake-prone coastal strip, the young land has not yet settled down, and according to Eugene Kojan of the State Division of Forestry's watershed study project, natural erosion rates here are among the highest in North America. It may be only a coincidence that California's nervous San Andreas Fault, which pierces the region from south to north like a troublesome nerve, is the same geological age as the tree, but there's no question that it has been one of the contributors to another situation preferred by the redwood: deep deposits of alluvial soil.

Where these favorable soil and moisture conditions combine, usually on streamside benches and in the valleys and canyons, sempervirens is capable of crowding more wood in the sky than any other timber species. Sonoma County's Big Bottom, which embraced part of what is now Armstrong Redwood State Park, contained one acre of trees that measured 1.5 million board feet. It would have built a foot-wide walkway of inch-thick boards from New York City north to the Canadian border. Some single acres have produced one million board feet, but the average yield in the big-timber country is 35,000 feet for Mendocino County, and 60,000 to 100,000 feet in Humboldt and Del Norte counties.

On most forest land in the Great Lake states, the East and South, stands of timber containing five thousand to ten thousand board feet to the acre are considered excellent.

Individual redwoods have been found that measure 100,000 to 200,000 board feet. One tree was reported at 361,000 feet, which, translated to lumber, was enough to build a community of thirty or more homes. There's the Church of One Tree in Santa Rosa, made from a single redwood cut three quarters of a century ago near the Russian River. It's big enough to hold five hundred people, and the builders wound up with enough shingles left over to roof several houses.

Such examples of good growing sites possess a strange combination of fog, rain, and ever-shifting soils that produces the taller, larger redwoods. But ideal sites are rare, and this has created a faulty impression for those living outside the Redwood Region—the great misunderstanding gap, as one forester calls it.

## Chapter III

## *The Two Forests*

With tunnel vision, films, postcards, books, and photographs picture the huge trees crowding the roadside, the majestic forests, the hollowed-out trunks that cars are driven through.

Automobile travelers, cruising along the Redwood Highway, plotted when the path of least resistance was to follow the river canyons, come to believe that all redwoods are like those about them—ancient giants two hundred or three hundred feet tall.

The world has long been looking at the heritage forest, whose image of stirring beauty is well fixed. But the conception that all two million acres of redwood-type forest land was once made up of superlative trees like these is approximately ninety-five percent wrong. It would be as reasonable to assume that all American cars are Cadillacs.

There are two distinct sempervirens forests, as different in their way as the rich crops grown in California's irrigated valleys and the lesser produce of the drier uplands.

For those who have never ventured more than a quarter mile from the road or clambered up a wooded sidehill, the faulty impression is understandable. The round stuff growing in the second redwood forest on the slopes usually isn't worth another look. Though it may be virgin old growth, it is likely to be less photogenic than its counterpart in other forest species across the land.

Conditions that produce the largest redwoods are rich, alluvial soil, abundant moisture and protection from wind. Where these circumstances combine, usually in valleys and along streamsides, the pure stands of superlative trees are found. Since nearly all the Redwood Region is mountainous, the relative amount of such areas is severely limited.

As the slopes get steeper, the altitude greater, the soil thinner, and the water supply scarcer, the redwood becomes smaller and then gives way to bald hills similar to those in the new national park, or disappears in a forest containing other species.

There are about two hundred different soil types in the region, and one of them in Mendocino County produces ancient, virgin redwoods less than twenty feet tall.

The disenchanting fact, according to a compilation of surveys made by California Redwood Association forester John T. Keane, is that the average diameter of most of the old redwoods is about the size of a large pizza.

Volume measurement is another means of separating the striking differences between the two sempervirens forests. Trees found on the lowlands—the valleys, flats, and benches —are five and a half times larger, on the average, than those growing on the slopes or uplands.

The U.S. Bureau of Forestry in 1903 called the slope-type forest fifty times more common than the lowland type. The Northern California Section of the Society of American Foresters in 1964 issued a more sophisticated estimate: the cream-of-the-crop bottom-land type amounts to a maximum of 100,000 acres.

If you've seen one redwood tree, you've seen them all, a candidate for governor of California is supposed to have said in the heat of the national park campaign. Quantitatively, he would have been right, considering that no person is likely to see all the redwoods now in state parks alone. Biologically, he would be dead wrong. The redwood comes in assorted sizes, shapes, and color shadings, making it difficult to label any forest stand as typical. With pleasing disarray, the region's woodland blanket is a greenish crazy quilt patched with many other types of trees and undergrowth that vary throughout the range.

In the lowland groves, the associated plants are primarily shade-tolerant and flood-resistant, such as the ferns and cloverlike sorrel. The sunnier upland forests provide many vegetative surprises. Springtime brings cream-colored aralia blossoms that compete with the spectrum tones of the azalea and rhododendron for a place in the sun. Later in the year, edible berries—huckleberry, thimbleberry, salmonberry, blackberry, and elderberry—lend their purples and pinks.

Wild flowers represent a wide range of those found elsewhere in the state, but only in the redwoods may the visitor come across the tiny stream orchids and rain orchids growing under creekside shrubs.

Among the cone-bearing trees, there will be hemlock, Sitka spruce, and Port Orford cedar intermingled in the northern forests. White fir is common. In one small area of southern Mendocino County, the giant sugar pine has moved across from the Sierra to keep sempervirens company.

Associated hardwoods include the madrona, alder, tan oak, chinquapin, coast live oak, and the common California laurel (also known as Oregon myrtle, pepperwood, or bay tree). Occasional counterpoint is provided by willows, buckeye, and big-leaf maple.

But the redwood's most constant companion is the Douglas fir. In the redwood-type forest as a whole it actually exceeds sempervirens in volume and acreage. And its abundant presence has contributed to further confusion about our supply of redwoods.

How many acres there once were and how many acres there are now was the great redwood numbers game that reached its peak of popularity during the recent national park campaign. Citizens for a Redwood National Park claimed that when the white man arrived, there were two million acres of *Sequoia sempervirens*. No, corrected spokesmen for the timber industry, there were only 1.5 million. The Sierra Club used both figures tellingly at one time or another.

To be charitable, all parties are close to correct. Unless traces of propaganda or exaggeration accompanied their use —a circumstance not unknown—the primary blame for confusion goes to the difficulty of defining a redwood forest, to the various measuring systems that have been used, and to whether the entire range or only the commercial forest is being considered.

In other forests, it is customary to type the land according to the single species that makes up fifty percent or more of the timber cover. But because most of the redwood's range is mixed forest, it has always received special treatment.

To spike down the section markers on this disputed terri-

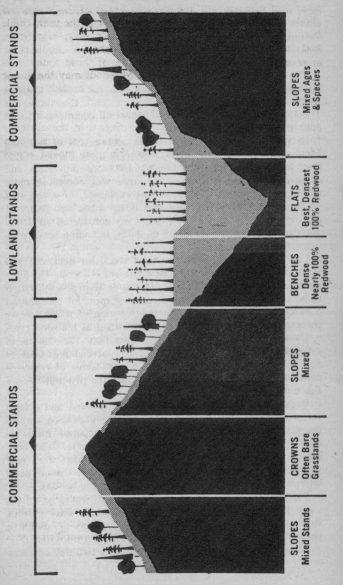

COMMERCIAL STANDS

SLOPES
Mixed Ages & Species

LOWLAND STANDS

FLATS
Best, Densest
100% Redwood

BENCHES
Dense
Nearly 100% Redwood

COMMERCIAL STANDS

SLOPES
Mixed

CROWNS
Often Bare
Grasslands

SLOPES
Mixed Stands

tory, it is necessary to learn whether the acreage figure includes the entire range of the species or disregards the noncommercial forest, which is tree-growing land withdrawn from logging. Government parks and reserves account for most of the noncommercial category.

The first authoritative estimate of the amount of commercial redwoods, those available for harvesting, came in 1925, when the U.S. Forest Service said the total was 1,454,000 acres, or about one fourth of all commercial forest land in the region.

In 1945 the service reported the acreage of the working forest as 1,879,000. No doubt there were those a quarter century ago who pointed to the 425,000-acre difference and claimed that here was proof the tree was becoming more abundant instead of scarcer. It was explained, however, that greater utilization of the tree was being made and many of the "merchantable" trees were not so considered in 1925. Also, more accurate measuring methods, including aerial photography, had been employed.

For the first time, a bold official stuck his neck out and tried to define the redwood-type commercial forest. The Forest Service's California Forest and Range Experiment Station ruled that an area with five percent or more of the ground covered by trees of any commercial species, of which twenty percent were redwoods, was to be classified as redwood type.

Using this so-called California definition, the station in 1954 declared the total acreage of commercial redwoods as 1,929,000. In addition there were 53,000 acres of noncommercial land, largely in state parks. Thus, the two-million-acre figure was born.

Because of the difference between the lowland and upland forests, with a very small area in pure, all-redwood stands, the California definition fails to give an accurate measurement. To use an extreme example, if an acre were one-twentieth covered with trees, of which one fifth were redwoods, it would then have to be classed a redwood acre, though only one percent of the acre contained redwoods.

The average redwood acre, if one existed, would be a little more than half covered by conifers of which sixty percent would be redwood, thirty-five percent Douglas fir, and five percent hemlock, spruce, white fir, and Port Orford cedar.

Those who prefer to say there were once two million acres

Tallest living trees in the world grow beside Redwood Creek in the new Redwood National Park. Libbey Tree at right measures 367 feet. The Grove of Giants was discovered in 1963 by a National Geographic Society party.

From the days of the Spanish and Mexican missions, redwood has been California's favorite wood for houses of worship. The chapel at Fort Ross State Historical Monument (top) dates from 1825 and is the oldest Russian Orthodox church in the country. It was built of timbers cut from the surrounding redwood forest. Both the old and new churches of Our Lady of Mt. Carmel (below) are of redwood; the new church is made of wood from ancient wine casks salvaged from the nearby Italian-Swiss Colony winery.

Outdoor laboratory is made up of stump sprouts from a stand of timber clear-cut forty-six years ago. Industrial foresters are studying the effects of thinning—the periodic removal of weaker redwoods that would eventually be crowded to death. With competition eliminated, the remaining trees add wood volume ten times faster than in unmanaged forests. Stumps continue to sprout new trees. By cropping the older trees after they have reached their fastest growth rate, the universal goal of forestry—maximum productivity of the land—can be achieved.

The wonder of the redwood forest is a never-ending delight to the observant. Cub Scouts are among thousands who enjoy Georgia-Pacific Grove on the Van Duzen River, part of the Tree Farm land open to the public under the Redwood Industry Recreation Areas program.

of redwoods may continue, though with the knowledge that this description is now generally considered misleading.

Recognizing the margin for confusion in the region's mongrel forest, federal agencies recently switched from the generous California definition to what is known as the Forest Survey definition. This requires a redwood acre to have twenty percent or more of the cubic volume of its trees in redwood, excluding areas which are ten percent or less covered with timber. In this case, the extreme produces an acre having only two percent redwood.

This Forest Survey definition in 1954 knocked off 330,000 marginal acres from the California definition to arrive at a total of 1,588,000 commercial acres.

The latest Forest Survey estimate made in 1963 shows 1,586,000 acres of redwood-type forest available for commercial harvesting.

Most acreage summaries ignore the ten thousand acres of redwoods in southwestern Oregon, much of which is in reserve or noncommercial status.

The people of the Forest Service and the Society of American Foresters are among those concerned with the confusion surrounding definitions of the redwood type. Both organizations are at work on a new measurement that will require a redwood acre to have fifty percent or more redwood trees. This is expected to provide a more realistic inventory, probably in the 1.2-million-acre range.

The new figure is not a danger signal that we are losing redwoods, for about ninety percent of the forest acreage of 1769 is still growing trees. Some of the lost land has not been properly restocked with new trees after logging. Repeated fires and overgrazing by livestock have claimed other marginal acreages. A large portion has been the victim of progress—highways, suburbs, agriculture, and dams.

What's left is more productive than ever. "Because of the inherent vigor of redwood," says a 1966 statement of the Society of American Foresters, "harvesting has resulted in young-growth forests with five to ten times the number of redwoods that were present in the original forest stand."

The greatest single loss of commercial forest land has been to parks and reserves. Close to ten percent of the original range is now preserved and is no longer included under the definition of commercial forest.

All authoritative sources agree that California in the mid-1960's had some 300,000 acres of virgin coast redwood forest, including about 75,000 acres in parks and reserves.

## COAST REDWOODS IN GOVERNMENT OWNERSHIP

| Agency | Acreage |
| --- | --- |
| California Department of Parks and Recreation | 119,415[a] |
| California Division of Forestry | 52,070 |
| National Park Service | 31,374[b] |
| U.S. Forest Service | 20,927[c] |
| County of San Mateo | 6,443 |
| U.S. Bureau of Land Management | 2,600 |
| Marin Municipal Water District | 2,600 |
| U.S. Bureau of Indian Affairs | 2,013 |
| City and County of San Francisco | 2,000 |
| Other public agencies | 8,565 |
| | 248,007 |

[a] Includes coast redwoods in parks not classified as redwood type, such as Austin Creek, Russian Gulch, Kruse Rhododendron Reserve and Bothe-Napa.
[b] Includes 2,431 acres authorized but not yet acquired.
[c] Includes approximately 13,000 acres subject to exchange under provisions of Redwood National Park Act.

The National Park Service in 1964 said there was an additional 450,000 acres of old-growth forest land where a minor amount of logging had taken place in the past. Their total was three quarters of a million acres of virgin and old growth. This, however, was based on the obsolete California classification and is confused further because of the varying definitions of old growth in use.

A more realistic appraisal may be found in the volume of timber instead of acreage. The Forest Service in 1963 reported a total of thirty-one billion board feet of standing redwood sawtimber (over eleven inches diameter) in commercial status. Of itself, this would be sufficient for something beyond thirty years of logging at the current rate. But there are also the fast-growing younger trees to consider. The Park Service study showed an additional fifteen billion board feet represented by trees under sixty years of age. This was twice the volume reported in 1948. The growth rate will double again by the end of the century.

### COAST REDWOOD ACREAGES

| | |
|---|---:|
| Range by "California" definition | 1,982,000 |
| Range by "Forest Survey" definition | 1,687,000 |
| Commercial redwood type | 1,500,000 |
| Virgin and old-growth forest | 750,000 |
| Virgin forest (defined on page 94) | 300,000 |
| State parks | 119,000 |
| Other parks and reserves | 57,000 |

It is this weedlike regrowth that the timber-products industry is counting on for its future source of raw material, and until recently, there seemed to be no cause for concern.

The greatest threat to the well-planned dream of continuous crops of trees, as state resources administrator Norman B. Livermore, Jr., puts it, is an uneasy balance in redwood land allocation that has developed without planning or coordination over the years.

Gradually, the public has become the largest of landowners in the redwoods. Government agencies hold half the volume of all virgin and old-growth timber, mostly in noncommercial status. At the same time, acquisition of tree-producing land for private homesites and recreational use has zoomed, forming the second pincer of a squeeze on the commercial forests. There are more than seven thousand private owners of redwood land over ten acres in size.

Livermore believes the loss of any more multipurpose commercial lands for single uses will be harmful to the economy and welfare of the people of the region, as well as an avoidable waste of the forest potential.

As the government agencies and private real-estate buyers

continue to nibble away at the productive land base, the squabbles over who owns how much seem unworthy of such a resource, so long as we can be sure the limited amount of land —all we'll ever have—is being properly managed for its highest and best use, whether that be for wilderness, agriculture, recreation, or timber production.

More than ever, the way the remaining commercial lands are managed is vital in making the most of the unequaled promise of the redwood.

For the first 150 years of logging, it didn't make much difference.

# Chapter IV

# *Big Hole in the Sky*

The awesome task of cutting down redwoods, getting logs to the mill, and shaping them into useful products is responsible for one of America's great industrial epics, written by a bold new breed of characters who conquered the last timbered frontier.

For a century and a half, those who have dared face such a tree, such a forest, have been independent, enterprising, and more than a little provincial. They offer reason to believe that if man's presence has affected the ecology of the redwood forests, then the process has worked the other way too, with some of the unusual qualities of the environment rubbing off on the humans who have chosen to live and work in it.

Lumberjacks who followed the westward tilt in the nineteenth century, fresh from the eastern pine country, looked at the tall red trees and remarked that they sure punched a big hole in the sky.

So tall it took a week to see to their tops, though seven men could do it in one day if they all looked together. Trees so big it took two liars to believe one.

In this hard country, as they called it, with its "slaunchandicular" terrain, woodsmen had to possess ingenuity, persistence, and sheer muscle power worthy of Paul Bunyan. In the strange and wonderful measures they devised for converting trees to boards, the brush pirates and splinter pickers used chewing tobacco, baling wire, and cuss words in about equal proportions.

Their surroundings inspired an unwritten code that made a handshake a contract and every stranger a friend. In an area long isolated from the rest of California, and where the demand for creation of a separate state is sometimes heard, the people retain a distinct regional character, perhaps consciously, reminiscent of the frontier. It might be pinpointed in the redwood tree faller's insistence on still being called a chopper, though he's been using a chain saw for thirty years.

They began from scratch, for there was no precedent in converting the mightiest forest on earth to man's use.

The Indians of the northern California coast had considered the redwood something to be admired, but feared and left alone. Its forests were valueless. Few game animals or birds were there, and the woods could be a lurking place for unfriendly tribesmen or an occasional man-killing grizzly bear. Trails usually went around, but those that ventured in were designed to reach open ground by the shortest route. Most of it was a damp, impenetrable tangle of fallen timber and undergrowth the Pomos called "the dark place."

Early white visitors shared the Indian viewpoint. Famed botanist David Douglas, stumbling through the Santa Cruz forests in 1830, wrote that the redwoods "give the mountains a most peculiar, I was almost going to say awful appearance." The exploring party that established the town of Eureka in 1849 found they could move through the redwoods no faster than two miles a day. Lewis K. Wood, diarist of the party, reported that to go around the trees was just as difficult as to go over them.

"We were obliged therefore, constantly to keep two men ahead with axes, who, as occasion required, would chop into and slab off sufficient to construct a sort of platform by means of which the pack animals were driven up on the log and forced to jump off on the opposite side."

It was redwood's usefulness as a product that made it a welcome gift to the Indians. They preferred its even grain and easy workability in shaping dugout canoes. With wedges, they split out rough boards and planks to build shelters and communal sweathouses.

There was then no need for tree felling. Nature did the job. When redwoods died of old age, enough of them toppled accessibly near the Indian settlements or floated up on the beaches. The only known "logging" was done by Indians near the Russian River; they built fires at the base of the redwoods to fell them, then collected the acorns stored by woodpeckers high up in the bark.

One of the first recorded uses of redwood as a product took place a year before America's Declaration of Independence. Lt. Juan Bautista de Ayala of the Monterey Mission party was ordered to explore the unknown waters of San Francisco Bay. He and his men found a large redwood log near the Carmel River and shaped up a dugout canoe with axes. Sailing northward for a hundred miles and eight days, he became the first to navigate the Golden Gate.

The Spanish colonists who came to California made surprisingly little use of the redwoods, probably because the logs were too large to handle. Then there were the unfriendly Indians, whose burning raids were responsible for the classic Monterey style of architecture, made of fireproof adobe-block walls and tile roofs.

But even an adobe structure needs wood for doors, beams, lintels, framing, and supports. The length of a room or building was often determined by the length of available timbers. In their experimenting, the Californios made use of local pine, oak, and sycamore—with a shipload of Australian eucalyptus thrown in—before they came to recognize the qualities of their backyard *palo colorado*.

The earliest redwood logging of consequence began in 1777 in the hills sloping down from present-day Skyline Boulevard, about fifty miles south of San Francisco. Where the logs had fallen, Indian workmen split off boards with wedges or used axes to hand-hew rough timbers, which were then taken by ox-drawn *carretas* to the new town of San Jose and the mission at Santa Clara.

Much of the wood was wasted by this method, so the first step toward conservative use might be considered the adoption of the sawpit. In Alta California, it was called an *aserradero*. This was a gravelike hole dug about six feet deep over which logs were rolled. One sawyer took his place atop the log and another, called the pitman, was in the hole. Using a four-foot-long whipsaw with handles at both ends, they ripped their way down the length of the log, taking about an hour to produce one board.

As the sawteeth were angled to work only in one direction —on the downstroke—the sweating pitman did most of the work and got all of the sawdust, making him a leading candidate for having the most unpleasant job in the history of the lumber business.

In the 1830's, Yankee whaling ships brought in seven-foot saws that helped double California's production of lumber. Sawpits were established in the redwood forests of what are now Monterey and San Benito counties, and near Aptos, Santa Cruz, Palo Alto, Oakland, Sausalito, and Bodega.

To enter the redwood business, all it took was an ax, a saw, wedges, and about thirty dollars cash. A fee of five percent of the value of the finished lumber was charged to cut timber on either government or private land.

The huge Ferris wheel-like paddle that marked a water-powered sawmill was a common sight along the streams of the United States and Europe long before it reached the redwoods. The first was erected in 1834 by John B. R. Cooper, ship captain-trader, who became a Mexican citizen and married a daughter of General Vallejo. His mill was built on remote Mark West Creek, near present-day Santa Rosa, where it served, incidentally, as the most northerly Mexican military outpost.

Cooper's short-lived factory, and those soon to follow, employed running water to turn a shaft that, by gears or belt, would then send a wood-framed ripsaw moving up and down. This was called a sash or muley saw.

The Russians peacefully invaded the realm of the dons in 1809 and, true to their racial idiosyncrasy, established a number of firsts. At Fort Ross, about seventy miles up the coast from San Francisco, the colonists operated a sawpit inside their redwood log stockade and in the 1820's became the first to export redwood lumber in any quantity. They were the first, also, to build large sailing ships on the Pacific Coast, though the redwood planks and green oak timbers they used proved a sodden, leaky combination.

By 1841, the Russian-American Company found they could not produce enough foodstuffs to feed the Alaskan colony or enough sea-otter furs for the mother country, and sold their possessions to Captain John Sutter. He moved most of the salvaged redwood lumber and timbers to his fort, then under construction at Sacramento, leaving intact the redwood chapel and the *comandante*'s house.

Another of the foreigners with faith in the future of California was Captain Stephen Smith of Baltimore. Impressed with the prospects of producing redwood lumber for both domestic and export markets, he brought a small steam engine and a motley crew of mechanics to California in 1843. At a site near Bodega, about fifty miles up the coast from San Francisco, he applied the state's first steam engine of any kind to run the West's first steam-powered sawmill.

A number of water-powered mills appeared in the lively 1840's, and the business of manufacturing redwood products overtook the earlier pursuits of farming, fur trapping, fishing, and livestock raising to become the most important industry in Alta California.

In these days of waning Mexican influence, land and timber were available almost for the asking. Governor Pío Pico alone handed out eighty land grants in his last year in office. By 1847, two thirds of the area where redwood grows, from Big Sur on the south to present-day Mendocino and Ukiah on the north, was claimed by private owners holding Spanish or Mexican deeds.

An important advance in lumber manufacturing—and by chance in conservation—came the same year. American occupation troops at Monterey imported a round iron saw from the East and started up the West's first circular mill. It was more efficient than the up-and-down saws and wasted less of the log. The familiar high whine of a buzz saw was missing, however, as this mill was powered by four mules, harnessed to shafts and a central hub, circling like a living merry-go-round.

The sleepy ways of this pleasant land ended suddenly when California became a U. S. territory and lumberman John Marshall discovered gold. Hordes of '49'ers piled in. For much of the redwood forest, the days of stillness were numbered.

For the first year of the Gold Rush, the redwood axmen and whipsawyers turned their backs on the fifty dollars a thousand board feet their produce was bringing and deserted to the irresistible lure of gold. As lumber prices climbed—five times, then as much as ten times higher in a few frantic years—the woodsmen returned. This time they had steam power, circular saws, and customers whose needs for lumber seemed insatiable.

The renewable green gold of the Sequoian forests over the years would turn out to be more valuable than all the glittering metal ever produced by the Mother Lode.

As for supplies of timber to feed the mills, Uncle Sam

turned out to be more generous than his Spanish and Mexican predecessors. The Pre-Emption Act of 1841 allowed citizens to pick up a quarter section of land for $1.50 an acre. For squatters, the law was conveniently retroactive.

The new state government of California needed money, not land. Its one-eighteenth share of the public domain was sold as fast as buyers could be found for $1.25 an acre, timber included.

When Congress passed the Homestead Act in 1862, offering 160 acres with no charge but a filing fee, there were still few takers in the unclaimed redwood forests. Timber at this time was a liability. Except for accessible strips, near towns and along the coast and larger rivers, loggers lacked the technological means of reaching more than a mile or so into the timber.

Unless there was gold under it, forest land would have to be cleared before it had any value and then only for livestock or farming. Elsewhere you could burn off the firs and pines to make way for crops, but with fire-resistant, stump-sprouting redwood this was no easy job. Nearly all the northerly redwood timber remained unclaimed. The best farmland in Mendocino County in the late 1860's was selling for as high as twenty dollars an acre; timber land went begging at five dollars.

The lumber mills that sprouted in the redwoods were usually located beside rivers and streams, where water was available for turning the wheels or supplying the steam engines. Here the trees grew largest and the water was a handy highway for floating logs.

Woodsmen rolled logs into the stream with the help of a hand-cranked jackscrew and the peavey, a long pole with a metal point and what appears to be half an ice tong at one end. The men who called themselves river pigs then took over, rafting the logs downstream or, by using small splash dams, flushing them toward the mill in a released torrent that occasionally broke the retaining booms and took an entire season's labor out into the Pacific Ocean.

Sometimes the logs were chuted off the hillsides into the water in V-shaped troughs formed by small logs.

The "candy shows" became scarcer as the timberline receded up the hillsides farther from the mill and a new method of moving the big sticks had to be found.

The redwood logger looked around and borrowed the ox-power idea of the Spaniards who had preceded him. With a few modifications, it became the skid road, a prepared trail from the stump to the landing or log-assembling area. In the eastern woods, lesser trees had been moved mainly by horse teams, usually on sleds or icy roads. But redwood country was made standing on end, they said, and horses were an underpowered rarity. Until steam power arrived, the prime mover of logs was the ox.

**"SNAKING OUT."**

The thousand-pound brutes were always called bulls, regardless of lineage or sex. In an extravagant gesture of respect for this fellow worker, the logger applied the term "bull" to anything he considered of notable proportions. Bull cable blocks and bull donkey engines, for example, were the largest of their kind.

The etymological heritage remains in terms such as "bull-buck" for the head man of the log-sawing buckers, "bull of the woods," and "bulldozer." The use of the word as an expletive can still be expressive in some circles, carrying with it a faint reminder of one of the occupational hazards of the nineteenth-century loggers who had to work around the animals.

A skid road could be merely a cleared roadway, as it is today. Earlier, it was often built by half burying twelve-foot-long logs crosswise to the path of the plodding teams. Notches were chopped in the widely spaced corduroy bed to keep the trains of three or four logs centered on the road.

Culturally speaking, the skid road of the woods and the skid road of today's cities are one. Since early skidding was from the forest down to waterfront lumber mills, where communities were developing, the pioneer sections of such western towns as Seattle, Portland, and Eureka were literally skid roads, a term now frequently corrupted to "skid row." Here among the flophouses, employment agencies, and saloons, it could be boisterous, quiet, or in between, a sort of audiovisual barometer of the lumber economy. Out-of-work woodsmen and millworkers were in residence, awaiting better times. It was the first and the last place honored by visits of recently paid loggers who had come to town to get their "teeth fixed." When visiting seamen, gamblers, and shady ladies were added to the volatile mix of humanity, the terminus of the original skid road for logs could be a hell-hole whose name was worthy of lasting usage.

While the low cost and practicality of the animal-powered skid road would keep it around until after the turn of the century, the woodsman's search for more efficient log-moving devices never ended. Some mills were located where bull power, chuting, or river driving was out of the question, and this brought about one of the lumber industry's greatest mechanical advances. It was the woods railroad, powered at first by horses and oxen, then steam locomotives and, in a few persistent cases, by Rudolf Diesel's smelly invention.

California's first railroad was a log hauler built by F. R. and A. J. Hooper in the Gold Rush days of 1852. The wooden-tracked, one-horse line served their mill at Trinidad, near the southern boundary of today's Redwood National Park.

Other little lines for hauling logs and lumber soon appeared around Humboldt Bay, including what is now the oldest regularly operating railroad in the West. It was called the Union Plank Walk, Rail Track, & Wharf Co. when organized in

1854. Motive power was a white work horse named Spanking Fury, whose job was to haul lumber and ship passengers on a two-mile-long wharf built on redwood pilings that may still be seen on the Bay mudflats near Arcata. Eleven decades later, the presently named Arcata & Mad River Railroad is still hauling redwood lumber for the Simpson Timber Co. and other firms. But Spanking Fury must be snorting in his grave; his successor is a diesel locomotive.

For the first hundred years of redwood logging, no saws of any kind were equal to the task of felling the big trees and loggers relied on the ax. It was a tedious job, often taking a two-man chopping team six days—each twelve hours long—to bring down a single tree. The woodsmen liked to tell newcomers a story about the time they chopped a week on one side of a redwood before discovering that another chopper had been working eight days on the other side of the same tree.

Standing on the ground, they were obliged to chip away at the widest part of the trunk. To get above the flaring butt formed on most redwoods, some ingenious axman of the last century devised the springboard system. A notch was cut in the trunk chest high off the ground, and a five-foot-long plank called a driver was inserted. If this height didn't please the loggers, they inserted more drivers at higher levels, springboarding their way up to the point where the first cut was to be made.

The high cut was made not only to save time, but also to eliminate the butt log, which was generally too large for the mill saws of the day and, being the heaviest part of the tree, often sank when dumped in the log pond. Handsaws replaced axes as the primary felling tool in the 1870's—another regional innovation—but the springboard system was retained for the further reason that the bark higher up the tree contained less grit to dull the sawteeth.

Since redwood stumps possess all the rot-free qualities of the species, forest visitors today wonder at the notched monuments, as high as ten or fifteen feet, they see scattered among the young trees.

High-stump waste was appalling, representing as much as twenty or thirty thousand board feet to the acre. Some split product makers are now salvaging the old stumps to produce grape stakes, shingles, and fence material.

On the job, the experienced chopper and his ax became

one. He could sculpture an undercut with hardly a ripple in it and set a tree down wherever he wanted it, some said even in the teeth of a northwest gale. His spare time was spent keeping the ax sharp enough to shave with, which he sometimes did.

Accuracy was part of the job. Unless carefully felled, a water-heavy redwood tree may split, shatter, or splinter when hitting the ground, leaving the crew with a pile of kindling wood, red faces, and the need for a new employer. The loss represented by carelessness—in time, money, and wood—can be impressive.

So once again, the unique redwood called for its own special treatment. With some modifications resulting from improved machinery and new skills, the procedure in bringing a tree safely to earth today is basically the same as that of the last century.

Following an inspection of the area by the woods superintendent, the bull chopper approached each selected tree with a pair of six-foot-long sticks joined to form a V. Standing against the trunk inside the triangle formed by the "sighting gun," he aimed its apex in the direction the tree was to be felled. He then drove a stake in the ground about one hundred feet out along the line of fall. "I've got a dime on that stake," he told the crew, "and I want a nickel change."

Then with a concern unmatched by loggers elsewhere in the world, the redwood choppers for ninety years have been dropping their trees into a bed to cushion the fall. Until tractors took over the bed-smoothing job a few decades ago, the layout was prepared by hand-piling brush and tree limbs along the stake line.

Either chopping or sawing with sixteen-foot-long "misery whips," the perspiring woodsmen skillfully brought the tree down and, in a feat that always impressed visitors to the woods, seldom failed to hit the sighting stake. As for the boss's dime, it will never be found. "We drove that stake clear through to China," choppers used to tell each other.

Down at the sawmills, the lumbermen were meeting and conquering challenges as formidable as those in the woods. The redwood logs being delivered to them might weigh as much as forty tons—dismaying to the millmen newly migrated from the forests of New England, New Brunswick, Pennsylvania, and the Great Lake states.

Their first chore was to reduce the log to a width suitable

for the puny mill saws of the day. This was done by wedge splitting lengthwise or by drilling holes in the log with an auger, tamping in black powder, and blasting it into half or quarter sections. A few poorly equipped mills continued the wasteful practice well into the twentieth century.

Among the pioneers who decided to enter this risky business were Irishman James Talbot Ryan and Canadian James Duff. Forming a partnership in 1852, they would demonstrate the daring, ingenuity, and perseverance that became commonplace—perhaps a necessity—in the redwoods.

Ryan, later a Congressman, was one of the first white men to see Humboldt Bay and surveyed the present town of Eureka with his own homemade transit. He persuaded former gold miner Duff to accompany him to San Francisco, where they bought an aging paddle-wheel steamer, loaded her deck with sawmill machinery, and proceeded up the coast. Crossing the treacherous bar at the mouth of Humboldt Bay, the mill machinery was washed overboard and, with it, the hopes of the partnership to help supply San Francisco's lumber needs.

Ryan would not give up. He hired laborers to dig a canal from the bay heading up one of the Eureka streets he had laid out. With a full head of steam, Ryan blew the whistle and rammed the steamboat into the bank between D and E streets. Here, the ship's engine was converted to a sawmill that was the first successful enterprise in the redwoods north of Sonoma County and the first to use steam power. This salty idea was not original. When the Parker House Hotel burned to the ground in one of San Francisco's many fires around 1850, its owner got together with some sharp operators and converted a ship's engine to power a steam sawmill across the bay at Sausalito. This redwood enterprise didn't last long, however, due to the intervention of the federal government. The steamship they had appropriated belonged to the U.S. Navy.

Hasty Kingburg Dodge, master of the steamer *Chesapeake*, beached his vessel a few miles south of Ryan and Duff in 1854, performed a similar conversion job, and rechristened her the Medina Mill.

Other ingenious attempts at automation were not lacking in the early days of the redwood business. The Mendocino Chinese colony in 1851 reportedly rigged up a muley saw powered by the incoming and outgoing tides of the ocean. R. S. Tyrell at Ferndale and F. E. Weston at Crescent City were among several who sawed wood by using horses hitched to a revolving capstan gear. The president of Mendocino City's only bank in the 1870's remembered a European practice begun fifteen centuries earlier and built an ill-fated sawmill powered by a windmill propeller.

The up-and-down sash saw of the mid-nineteenth century was modified after the circulars arrived, and was now called a gang saw because it had several saws mounted side by side and could slice off more than one board at a time.

The largest of the gang mills were cutting around eight thousand board feet of lumber a day, and local carpenters hauled it away, they claimed, faster than it could be manufactured.

Abruptly, the western lumber industry changed after the Civil War from docile infant to lusty adolescent. In the redwoods the growth came from the simultaneous arrival of new markets for lumber, improved transportation, steam-powered logging equipment, and more efficient mill machinery. It was the beginning of the highball days—named for the double blast of the steam whistle that signaled go ahead.

For half a century it was an era of high lumber production, careless logging practices, and, sometimes, cut-out and get-out. Who gave a damn for the next crop of trees, if any.

The power behind the highball days was steam. With steam trains instead of freight wagons, the three transcontinental lines that opened in the 1870's and 1880's could speed redwood lumber to markets anywhere in the nation. In the other direction, railroads were making westerners out of easterners at the greatest rate since the Gold Rush. The newcomers of California's "big boom" needed lumber, and their demands helped double the production of redwood between 1860 and 1880, and double it again in the next decade.

The iron horse found a job out in the forest, too. Though at first they were underpowered castoffs from the main line railroads, the rolling teakettles quickly replaced the horse-powered wooden railways and bull teams in getting logs to the mill.

The terrain of the Redwood Region has more ups and downs than a muley saw, and there were some places where even the audacity of the loggers and ever-improving locomotive power could not make the grade. With the aid of steam, loggers put together the power incline, a stretch of railroad track leaned against a hillside over which loaded log cars could be raised or lowered by cable. Some of these up-and-down railways angled close to thirty degrees, a match for San Francisco's cable cars.

Pioneer Eureka lumberman John Dolbeer thought more could be done with steam in the woods, and in 1882 patented a machine having a winding drum for winching logs by cable from the stump to the railroad or skid road. The Dolbeer donkey, it was called, because it couldn't raise enough steam to be rated in horsepower. But its portability and usefulness proved out and soon every logging show in the West would have at least one.

For an encore the following year, Dolbeer placed one of his machines on the front of a railroad locomotive and used the same steam from its boiler to pull both logs and trains.

The introduction of wire cable at this time replaced the ever-breaking Manila rope and made some fancy new log-handling tricks possible. First came the ground-lead system, which bumped in logs over stumps and along the ground to the donkey. A later development was the high-lead system, of ruthless power, by which cables attached to delimbed spar trees dragged and swung the logs in.

The ultimate was reached in the 1920's with the skyline, or flyer, system, which looked like the high wire of a daring circus acrobat and was as fascinating to watch. The skyline was a stationary cable supported 150 feet off the ground by two or more limbless spar trees. A pulleylike "bicycle," or flyer with logs dangling below, raced along the wire to the landing by skimming over stumps, trees, or canyons.

Improved metals made it possible by the 1870's to manufacture the oversized handsaws suited to the redwoods. Using these twelve- to sixteen-foot-long backbreakers, two men could fell one or two trees a day.

Down at the mill—better known as the sawdust factory—improved steam power about doubled production capacity. Some of the large plants could cut a hundred thousand board feet a day.

Mill saws became bigger and faster. The simple circular buzz saw was replaced by the double circular, one saw above another, which by cutting from the top and bottom at the same time processed a log twice as thick as a single saw. Then came the triple circular, which simultaneously sliced off the top of the log. Eight-footers could now be sawed.

In these rough-and-tumble days when "Give 'er snoose!"

(more steam power) was the byword, there was an early flicker of the light of conservation. It came in the form of the band saw, a continuous belt of steel whose whirring teeth could chew into any size log. The first one in the redwoods went into the Union Lumber Company mill in 1885. But the band saw was not designed to increase production. It would not catch up to the output of circulars until more powerful engines came along years later. Its value was in saving something like five or ten percent of once-wasted wood by making thinner cuts and creating less sawdust. And only a few logs had to be split by dynamite in order to fit the limits of the saws.

Along most of the redwood coast, small sailing schooners were the only means of getting redwood lumber to market for one hundred years. In the 1870's, the newly developed compound steam engine had been put aboard some of the windjammers as auxiliary power and by 1880 the first of the specially built steam schooners was launched. This little half-breed vessel could deliver lumber to San Francisco and southern California ports about twice as fast as sail alone and would dominate the Pacific coastal trade until World War II.

Most of the doghole ports, so-called because there was just about enough room for a dog to turn around in, had no piers or docks. Until the '80's lumber was loaded aboard ship from shoreside cliffs by sliding it down wooden chutes. This was supplanted by the steam-powered wire-chute system. At several dozen mill "ports" of the redwood coast, lumber, produce, livestock, breathless passengers, and all were loaded on a swaying platform and taken on and off ship over a cable slung between shore and the ship.

Venturesome redwood lumbermen tried to overcome the difficulties and high costs of shipping their lumber out by building enormous, cigar-shaped rafts of logs, held together by chains, to be towed down the Pacific for processing by mills around San Francisco and even San Diego bays.

The first attempt from Fort Bragg wound up as driftwood along one hundred miles of beach. But another try turned out to be the first successful deep-water rafting venture on the Pacific. Redwood's water-heavy qualities later proved too risky for ocean rafting, but the practice continued with other West Coast species. These floating woodpiles delivered more than a billion board feet of logs in their fifty-year heyday.

The final migration of America's lumbermen began in the 1880's. With the end of their timber supplies in the Great Lake states in view, they sought new frontiers. Some turned to the pineries of the South, but most came West. Many settled in the redwoods, awed alike by the quality of the timber and the unequaled difficulty in logging it out.

One of them, seeing a redwood log for the first time, is supposed to have remarked, "The man who cut that tree is a damned liar!"

Suddenly there was no more redwood frontier. All the forests had been spoken for. The newcomers helped double and triple the price of an acre of redwood land to a new high of one hundred dollars in 1900.

Stumpage, or standing timber, is valued on three things: market demand, quality of the wood, and accessibility to markets. The many changes affecting these elements would double the cost of an old-growth acre in another decade and send it up to six hundred dollars by the end of the 1920's. "You darn fool, why didn't you buy back then?" redwood lumbermen chide each other in a favorite pastime of California natives. The same land, when available, today sells for five or ten times as much.

The social, technological, and economic changes of the late Victorian era combined to produce a revolution in the business of producing lumber. Everything was speeded up. Some mills, they claimed, were running thirty hours a day. From the cutting of trees in the forest to the distribution of finished lumber, a new efficiency was evident.

Too efficient, thought some concerned citizens. The steam-powered cable logging systems used throughout America's forests smashed down young trees and anything else left in the way. Cutover land was being burned off for grazing. Wildfires were usually left to burn themselves out, unless threatening human lives and property. The enticements of new markets caused overcutting of the forests in some areas. From 1880 to 1900, the population of the United States increased fifty-two percent; the production of all species of lumber increased ninety-four percent.

The debut of the American Forestry Association in 1875, then the American Forestry Congress seven years later focused attention on the threats to the forests. In 1885 California became the first in the nation to establish a state board of forestry. A few years later the federal government tightened up on enforcement of the homesteading and free-timber laws and added the first units of the national forest system.

California received a Forest Protection Act and the nation's first state forester in 1905.

For a dozen years, President Theodore Roosevelt and his chief forester, Gifford Pinchot, hammered at America's conservation conscience.

Except for the preservation of outstanding examples of the forest, there seemed little need for conservation measures in the redwoods where, by the turn of the century, only ten or fifteen percent of the "limitless" forests had been touched. Any newfangled forestry measures would have to pay their way in order to keep redwood lumber prices in line with fir, pine, and spruce, for now a hopeless impossibility.

Lumber needed to rebuild San Francisco after the firequake of 1906 brought redwood production to a record of 650 million board feet, a high that would not be reached again until 1949. For the following quarter century, World War I and Coolidge prosperity notwithstanding, the output of some fifty redwood mills leveled off between the four hundred and six hundred million mark.

In the woods, Dolbeer's little donkey had undergone Frankensteinean changes. The logging engine developed into a two-hundred-ton skidding, yarding, and loading monster capable of sending cable tentacles half a mile into the forested gulches and valleys. It was hell on wheels, the most destructive piece of machinery ever to work the redwoods, recalls one forest manager.

The opening of the Panama Canal in 1914 meant new eastern markets to all Pacific Coast lumbermen. But in the northern Redwood Region, its effect was overshadowed by the driving of the last spike in the rail link between Eureka and San Francisco Bay. A half-dozen lumber-company feeder lines, such as the California Western and the Arcata & Mad River, joined rails with the new Northwestern Pacific Railroad. For the first time, the mills of the north coast could serve the growing central and southern California markets better than the perennial competition from the Pacific Northwest.

More than five decades later, Northwestern Pacific is still the region's only major railroad, and gets eighty percent of its income from hauling forest products.

One by one, the larger mills south of San Francisco shut down in the first quarter of the century. The easy timber had been removed after a hundred years of logging and there was then no market for the new-growth trees. Many thousands of acres of virgin timber remained in the mountains of Santa Cruz and San Mateo counties, as much of it does today, because its location was economically inaccessible.

In the mid-1920's, about eighty percent of all redwood production was coming from north of San Francisco, including about five percent from Oregon.

The depression that struck in 1929 was disastrous to the timber-dependent north coast. Redwood lumber production in three years skidded sixty-five percent to the same 135 million board feet it had been at the beginning of the steam era in 1880. Only two large mills were able to keep going with any regularity. Hammond Lumber Company lost eight million dollars. Foreclosures and bankruptcy struck many others.

"I'd burn the mill down," quipped one hard-pressed lumberman, "except I can't afford the insurance."

Aside from the human suffering and financial losses the Depression brought, it marked one of the bright points in the history of man in the redwoods.

The half century of highballing was over.

It was a time for cutting lumber prices, payrolls, and operating costs. In the woods, the steam railroads and logging machines were found to be using too much manpower input for the horsepower output. Operators looked enviously at their counterparts in the flatter fir and pine regions who had long ago begun converting to smaller, more economical gasoline and diesel-powered machinery. In redwood country, the terrain was too steep and the logs too big for any alternative to steam.

Only in 1934, after several years of development and field experiments did Caterpillar Tractor Company and Allis-Chalmers come up with diesel tracklayers worthy of the redwoods. The pioneer cats were as clumsy as a tipsy logger at the Saturday-night dance, but they were soon bringing in the big sticks at logging shows in five counties.

At the same time, an ingenious Forest Service man in Oregon took an old horse-drawn dozer, a primitive type of earth-scraper blade, attached it to the front of a logging tractor, and christened it a bulldozer. First used to build fire-protection trails in the forest, it was soon modified by Ed

Stamm of Crown Zellerbach and David Mason of Simpson Timber Company and assigned to carving out truck roads for log hauling.

The six percent of redwood logs hauled by trucks in 1931 jumped in a few years to more than fifty percent. Overnight, the steam railroad and its companion machinery for dragging in logs was doomed.

From the mid '30's on, the bulldozer was available to push roads almost anywhere in the forest, the tractor could maneuver among standing trees without damaging them, and the truck was on hand to roller-coaster the logs down to the lumber millpond.

The costs of logging were cut almost in half. For the first time small and isolated tracts of timber could be logged economically. And selective logging—the take-some, leave-some conservation practice of the pine country—could be applied where necessary.

The redwood operators now took another look at the costs of bringing down a tree.

Elsewhere in the country, the larger the tree, the lower the cost of preparing it for the mill. But the two or three days it took a pair of choppers to fell a redwood and then handsaw it into sixteen- to forty-foot lengths was sometimes a losing proposition.

The Pacific Lumber Company in 1923 pioneered the use of "portable" 150-pound gasoline-powered saws to buck felled redwoods into log units. The clumsy dragsaws had to be wheeled from place to place and were unable to cut horizontally for felling trees on the stump.

With the advent of the lightweight aluminum motor in the mid-1930's, the first practical "tree-felling machines" appeared. A pioneer five-horsepower model saved two thirds the time formerly needed to make logs out of a standing tree.

The great advantage of the chain saw was its ability to cut the tree trunk close to the groundline. Gone were the chopper's platforms and the high stumps left behind in the handsaw days. About ten to fifteen percent more of each tree could be sent down to the mill.

In the redwoods, economy was the mother of invention. In overcoming their Bunyan-sized problems, the people of woods and mills had applied a near-inspired ingenuity to cut costs. The fact that technological economy meant saving timber, and resulted in the need to cut fewer trees, was incidental or accidental.

If the leaders who emerged in the nineteenth century were called timber barons, in common with those of other industries, the title was not hereditary and was almost always earned in the redwoods by hard work. It was no business for dilettantes or hidden management. Fortunes were made or lost overnight on the whims of how much the public would pay for boards. Competition from other species of lumber has always been strong, and millmen sent their produce out on schooners, wagons, and railroad cars not knowing whether the returns would bring riches, disaster, or mere survival.

Among them was onetime logger Robert Dollar, tough as redwood bark, who could find no shipping company willing to risk picking up lumber from his new redwood mill located at the dangerous port of Usal. So he bought a leaky old steam schooner of his own. The *Newsboy* was the first vessel in what became America's largest merchant fleet.

A. B. Hammond began as a choreboy in the woods at seventeen and eventually created a three-state empire that included the redwood company lately acquired by Georgia-Pacific Corporation.

Red-headed C. R. Johnson, aged twenty-three, borrowed some capital in the mid-1880's and put together the sprawling Union Lumber Company, since 1968 a division of Boise-Cascade Corporation.

Mill Valley lumberman William A. Richardson laid out the town of Yerba Buena, since renamed San Francisco, and erected its first building of redwood. The community's first Protestant church and religious service were contributed by Reverend William Taylor, who financed his parish with a logging-milling operation in the East Bay redwoods.

Thomas Larkin, the first and only United States consul to the Province of Alta California, was the leading redwood lumberman of the Monterey Bay area in the 1830's. Among the colorful pioneers working in the southern redwoods were John Bidwell, later to be a U.S. presidential candidate on the Prohibition ticket; Peter Lassen, since memorialized by the mountain and national park bearing his name; and Harry Love, who captured the murderer Joaquin Murietta and used his reward money to buy a redwood mill seven miles north of Santa Cruz. Col. John Fremont operated a mill at San Jose.

Examples of success are common in a century and a half of Yankee enterprise in the redwoods, though this is an industry that has been hit by forest fires, floods, strikes, earthquakes, price wars, shipwrecks, tidal waves, mill fires, and financial panics, all disastrous to some.

Not all were of heroic mold. Among the culls was the flamboyant Harry Meiggs, who built San Francisco's second lumber mill at Fisherman's Wharf in 1850, was elected a city official, and went on a permanent vacation in South America with $45,000 of the taxpayers' money.

It's no longer possible to duplicate the Horatio Alger sink-or-swim success stories of the millhands, loggers, sailors, and farmers who entered the redwood business with high hopes, a few tools, and thirty dollars, and in the process fulfilled most of the dreams and aspirations of nineteenth-century Americans. Today's major companies are complex production and distribution structures, owned by 100,000 stockholders who employ skilled professionals as managers. But the same spirit that conquered the greatest logging and milling problems ever known has been evident in more recent years as men of the industry undertook the nation's first cooperative program of public recreation on private forests, pioneered the use of aerial photography in forest management, set up the state's first aerial fire prevention patrol and set aside, or in a dozen instances donated, their choicest timber lands for public park purposes.

Those who survived the hazards of the redwood business built well. Except for temporary closures due to strikes, fires, or depressions, the average length of continuous operation in the same forests, and in some cases on the same millsites, of California Redwood Association's seven member companies is an impressive eighty-one years. Two firms have celebrated their centennial.

Looking back on the formative years of the regional character, it seems the men of the redwoods had to possess some qualities shared by few others: good business sense, audacity tempered by an awareness of hazards, a dirty-overalls familiarity with logging and milling practices, and more than a dash of damfool luck. Their enterprise, to a greater extent than any other industrial group, helped build the Redwood Region and its capital city of San Francisco. Free men of strong character, they were, by chance of time and the redwoods, the last individualists.

## Chapter V

# *Bulls, Cats, and Donkeys*

The greatest industrial show on earth plays each day to an empty house out in the redwood forest. It begins soon after dawn with the persistent whine of the chain saw, ending at dusk when fog and a deeper silence envelop the stage.

The daily tasks of "letting daylight into the swamp" are never the same, even in the timeless redwoods. Every logging chance, every tree is different, presenting a new set of problems for the woodsmen to resolve.

At first glance, the self-styled "timber beast" doesn't seem much changed from his nineteenth-century predecessor. He wears the traditional spiked boots, nondescript shirt, and suspenders that hold up a pair of stagged, high-water pants. He carries a generous-sized lunch bucket, still called a nose bag from the days of horse logging, as part of the uniform equipment, and because smoking is usually prohibited on the job, he chews tobacco or inhales snuff.

Some of the job titles of the woods remain the same after fifty or a hundred years. There are hook tenders, donkey doctors, whistle punks, chasers, and rigging slingers.

But the logger's life-style has changed considerably from the days when he moved from job to job with a bedroll on his back. He usually lives in his own home, and if he's not picked up at the door by a company bus—still called a crummy from the crew car of railroad logging days—he drives to work. It's likely he's a family man, owning a color TV set, a power mower, and a house mortgage as impressive as any big city dweller's.

When new machinery and new tools came to the woods, the logger could no longer rely on the power of muscles and cuss words and was transformed to a skilled, well-paid professional.

Regardless of automated changes, the art of logging is still hard work. It begins when a "set" of two choppers, wearing tin safety hats, applies the chain saw to the trunk of a tree. The fluctuating wail commences, and under a shower of sawdust, the wedge-shaped undercut is made facing the long, narrow bed being prepared by a tractor.

The whirring teeth become smoking hot from friction, and the loggers take turns pouring a lubricating oil, usually nicknamed something like cougar juice, over the endless chain.

As the horizontal backcut is made on the opposite side of the trunk, plastic wedges and shims are sledgehammered into the narrow opening to prevent bind on the saw and to further guide the direction of fall. About halfway through the tree, where the bite of the six-foot-long saw approaches the undercut, the motor is shut off. In the sudden silence, the cry of "Up the hill!" is heard. Slowly, the tree leans, then with a loud crack gathers speed and whooshes thunderously into the bed.

The job of the falling team done, men called buckers move in to remove limbs from the prone trunk, and with chain saws slice off truck-length logs forty feet long. A tractor snakes through the standing trees, hooks on a log or two, and weaves back to the landing. Here a mobile loader is waiting to lift the logs onto trucks for the trip to the mill.

Tree felling, the foresters insist, is not the final act in the continuing drama of forest renewal, but the first. In achieving the goal of forestry everywhere—management of the land for its greatest productive capacity—it is necessary to imitate nature and replace declining trees with vigorous young ones. Some now believe that the process is important in perpetuating the sempervirens as a species.

Throughout the history of redwood logging, there have been two basic methods of harvesting. Clear-cutting, sometimes called block cutting or clean logging, removes all the trees from a limited area, usually no farther than five hundred feet from the nearest standing seed trees. The alternate practice is known as selective cutting, in which chosen trees are removed, but a specified number of seed trees eighteen inches in diameter or larger are left behind to reseed between the stump sprouts.

The forester's decision whether to clear-cut or selectively log an area is based on such considerations as soil type, lay of the land, climate, and the species, age, and condition of the trees. He is further hemmed in by state laws, needs of the lumber mill, and status of the company's sustained-yield program.

If the text-book principles of forestry are followed, the choice is usually not a difficult one, says Chief Forester Herbert Peterson of Simpson Timber Co. and a member of the State's Coast Range Forest Practice Committee. It is based on the simple objective of obtaining the greatest return from mature timber, protecting the watershed, and getting the new crop growing quickly.

Selective logging, which land managers refer to as uneven-aged forest management, recreates and speeds up the ever-changing natural conditions of the forest. All ages of trees are represented. Logging out the old trees imitates the natural falling of mature trees in the virgin forest. Young trees slowly work their way up to the hole left in the umbrella of branches and become a part of it.

This system evolved accidentally from the pioneer era, when loggers left some trees standing because they were too large, too small, or otherwise unsuited to the limited technology of the day.

Later, when it was found that these residual or leave trees helped reseed any gaps left between the sprouting of cut stumps, a conscious effort was made to apply the take-some, leave-some method already common in the western pine country.

The Forest Service has found that as few as three residual redwoods are capable of fully reseeding an acre. Parent trees scatter seeds a distance of about two football-field lengths, though winds might take them as far as two miles.

Another benefit of selective cutting is termed accelerated release growth. Trees left behind from logging can eventually add an amount of wood volume ten or twenty times greater than if the forest had remained unlogged. When the competition for light, moisture, and growing space is removed, residual trees are "released" and grow as much as fifty percent more volume each year. The inch or so in diameter that a suppressed tree may have added in eighty years can become an inch each year after logging has opened the forest canopy.

This type of logging, redwood operators are frequently reminded, has the advantage of being less conspicuous to the passing public. Some tree farms have been selectively logged two or three times, though the average tourist is unaware of it.

Selective logging is not advisable for all redwood stands. The Redwood Region is actually a sub-region of the Pacific Coast's extensive Douglas Fir Region, where climate and terrain make clear-cutting, or even-aged stand management, the universally accepted practice for better forestry. Experience and continuing studies show that selection management in some areas can be wasteful of timber, harmful to the watershed, or a hindrance to prompt reforestation.

The major reason for blockcutting, according to the foresters, is that commercial redwoods are seldom found in pure stands. There are usually whitewoods and hardwoods intermingled. While the redwood will quickly regenerate itself after logging with stump sprouts or seeds, the other species need help, and the instant forest created by aerial reseeding is called for. This requires cleared areas with a disturbed soil receptive to seeds. And unlike redwood, other young conifers generally cannot grow in shade.

Clear-cutting is recommended also where trees left standing after selective logging would be exposed to unusual conditions inviting windthrow or sunscalding.

Prompt reforestation prevents the growth of weeds and undesirable species that are not only a forest fire hazard but slow up the comeback of the conifers.

Until the arrival of the petroleum-based technology in the 1930's, most logging operations skinned off every tree from large areas of land. This was done at first with bull teams, then small donkey engines, and later by the devastating combination of the steam railroad and huge, steam-powered logging machines. Accompanied by the clanking, hissing, chugging sounds of a devil's worship, the iron monsters grabbed at the forest, knocking down everything that hindered the job of getting logs to the mill. Little concern was given to soil and watershed values or the next crop of trees. To make the costly operation pay, large areas had to be stripped before the rails could be picked up and relaid in the next watershed.

The redwoods always returned, eventually, but it was without credit to man and his machinery.

When World War II boosted demands for lumber, California timbermen and legislators alike became concerned about how some forest land was being treated. In 1943, a state senate forest study committee was created, and Professor Fritz became its consultant.

Their report two years later became a model for other states. It resulted in reorganization of the Board of Forestry, the acquisition of fifty thousand acres of redwoods for Jackson State Forest and passage of the Forest Practice Act, a far-reaching set of regulations designed to maintain healthy forests and a healthy forest economy.

Under the Act, today's clear-cutting is done on much smaller areas. The land must be reforested within five years after logging, either by artificial seeding, hand planting of seedlings, or natural reproduction. If the regrowth is considered inadequate, Division of Forestry inspectors may order the landowner to comply, or after public hearing, have the work done by the state with the owner receiving the bill.

Most of the time, the clear-cuts are reseeded immediately by a helicopter that flies across eight acres a minute, spewing out seeds from a fanlike device in the manner of a farmer's old hand-cranked grain seeder.

In the early days of experimenting with aerial reseeding, hungry birds, rabbits, mice, and ground squirrels would eat up the seeds almost as fast as they were dropped. It was found that by coating the seeds with silver paint, birds left them alone, probably because they no longer looked like seeds. Then by adding a chemical substance repellent to animals, it was possible to discourage the four-footed marauders too.

The state laws apply only to private timberland, but the clear-cutting and regeneration formula is commonly practiced on redwood forests owned by the U.S. Forest Service, the Department of the Interior, and the State Division of Forestry. Through continuing studies, the government foresters have found that reforestation is accomplished quickly by nature, and artificial seeding or planting is often unnecessary.

Researcher Kenneth M. Boe of the Yurok Experimental Forest used boxes to trap the seeds falling on twenty-two acres that had recently been clear-cut. He counted 200,000 to the acre, all sound, dropped by surrounding redwoods. It takes but five hundred to a thousand germinated seeds to cover an acre with new trees.

Both selective cutting and clear-cutting are regulated by

the act, which the Society of American Foresters considers the most advanced of seventeen similar state laws in the nation. Specific logging practices are detailed, along with fire-protection methods and erosion control. All operators must be registered, pay an annual fee, and obtain a permit before logging. Some counties of the region require local permits as well.

While observers agree the Act has been a great influence in bringing conservation to California's forests, some admit it is not perfect. You can't legislate nature, and the necessary built-in flexibility of man's laws have been subject to past abuses and mistakes. Four district committees administer the rules and pass on logging permit applications for approval by the State Board of Forestry. They are helping the Division of Forestry to gradually plug up the holes. The legislature amends the law from time to time, the most significant recent change being one that shifts responsibility for proper practices from the logging operator, who may not own the land, to both the operator and the landowner.

The ever-tightening laws have an indirect effect in protecting the scenic, fishery, and watershed values of California forests, though that is not their primary purpose, and in most cases there is duplication of intent in the existing Water Pollution and Fish and Game codes.

The cry of something like "Save the Watersheds" is now heard almost as often as "Save the Redwoods." It is an equally appealing, well-meaning objective designed to protect the land that produces redwoods. But behind it is an immensely complicated collection of natural and man-influenced factors that has caused State Forester Francis Raymond to warn that strong medicine hastily applied before diagnosis is not the cure.

Those who would restrict redwood logging to protect watershed values usually cite the devastating floods that hit the region—and the entire Pacific West—in 1964-65, and the tragic loss of several hundred old trees in the Rockefeller Forest from the Bull Creek flood ten years earlier.

Weather Bureau records show that the narrow redwood belt contributed very little to the north coast's "thousand-year flood" of the 1960's, almost all of the runoff coming from the Eel, Klamath, and Van Duzen watersheds outside the region as far as one hundred miles away. All government agencies concerned dismissed logging as a significant factor.

As for the 1955 flood at Bull Creek, a University of California symposium and other studies have failed to give conclusive evidence that logging in the upstream fir forests was a major cause of the huge wall of water that suddenly swept across the Rockefeller Forest. Most professionals have concluded that while all types of land management practices in the basin could have been improved, the largest share of the blame goes to one of the unpredictable natural acts of violence which mark the geologic and meteorological history of the area. The much-higher flood waters of 1965 did no damage to the old trees on Bull Creek flat.

Neither the redwood industry nor alarmed conservationists have come up with any convincing scientific evidence about the relationships between logging and floods. Studies made elsewhere have little relevance because of the region's unique geologic conditions, the unequaled regrowth powers of the redwood and its widespread root system that lives on after logging. The only survey that comes close was made by state and federal agencies in the Dos Rios basin of the Eel River's South Fork, and it showed the hooves of deer and cattle to be the primary causes of sheet erosion.

Most authorities go along with Dr. Rudolph Becking of Humboldt State College who concluded unhelpfully in a 1967 National Science Foundation report that "it may be premature to evaluate the effects of vegetative cover, especially forest cover, upon the streamflow in the Redwood Region."

The Pacific Southwest Forest and Range Experiment Station has turned to computers in the tough job of analyzing streamflow and sediment production data for the redwood forests.

The record of voluntary, unpublicized measures taken by a number of redwood operators gives hope that there is a golden rule of self-enlightened land management supplementing whatever laws may be on the books.

Witness Simpson Timber Co., operating along the fish-famous Klamath River, which expensively logs with special procedures to protect the shoreside scenery on its property, and puts loggers to work cleaning up tributary streams after each operation.

On the lands of Miller Redwood Co., adjacent to Redwood National Park, Chief Forester Richard Brown likes to show visitors the west branch of Mill Creek. Once a barrier to migrating fish because of natural debris and windfalls not connected with logging, it has been cleaned out by company employees diverted from regular duties.

Arcata Redwood Co. recently hired a former watershed specialist of the U.S. Forest Service to map the soil types on every acre of its property as a guide to erosion-free logging operations and road building.

Masonite Corp. is among several firms operating private logging roads having erosion-control standards exceeding those of government agencies.

Boise-Cascade Corp. has turned back the clock eighty years, reverting to logging by horses in a steep area where tractors might send too much silt into the stream below.

Such measures to protect forest-related values are commonplace, according to the Redwood Region Conservation Council, which estimates that since 1960, for example, one thousand miles of the region's streams have been opened or kept open to passage of migrating steelhead, salmon, and trout as an integral part of normal logging operations.

Whether voluntary or required, these steps add to the costs of logging, whose goal is to deliver the log from stump to mill as cheaply as possible. Hardest hit are the region's hundred or so independent logging contractors, known as a gyppos for their occupational need to travel from job to job like gypsies, who own no timber and have no control over log market prices. They are less able than larger, integrated companies to absorb the added expenses of what one of them calls "manicuring the forest."

This cost pressure is something like a vise, with the buyer of wood products acting as the immovable base. Despite the opinion of the do-it-yourself carpenter that prices at the local lumberyard will never stop rising, there is an economic point of no return. It is when the consumer turns to less-expensive substitute materials.

Logging costs are rising throughout the nation's forests as a by-product of the movement to improve our environment, and in some cases, because of the landowner's self-interest in demonstrating that private forest practices can be as good or better than those on government lands.

Redwood will probably be better able than other lumber species to withstand the added costs of improved logging techniques because of the constant demand for its desirable qualities, which, for now at least, have no rival—natural or man-made.

# Chapter VI

# *The Wonder Wood*

Naturalist Roger Ravelle of Harvard University spoke to fellow members of the American Association for the Advancement of Science at their 1969 convention and challenged them to invent a plastic that would look, feel, and act like redwood.

No doubt if man had set out to invent a most useful renewable resource, the incredible redwood would be among the top priorities. But science has quite a task; this plant and its wood is a supremely inimitable product of nature. For proof, take a trip through the lumber mill, where the strange structure of the wood is carefully unwrapped.

Dripping wet, the twenty-foot-long log, weighing twice as much as a passenger car, climbs slowly out of the log storage pond and like some formless monster from the deep rises up the escalator chain to enter the mill. It is midpoint in the journey between the forest and a hundred kinds of useful products. Inside the barnlike walls of this noisy manufacturing plant, the sectioned trunk will be sawn, peeled, glued, steamed, ground, or pressed, and in the fascinating process, redwood will once again earn its title of the tree of surprises.

"If God ever made a perfect material for man's use, this is it," says the unsentimental-appearing manager of a Mendocino County lumber mill. Looking out across the log pond to a timbered hillside, he suggests that the forests have transmitted some of their superlative qualities to the redwood as a product.

The reason for a lumberman's admiration is that, among

commercial softwoods, redwood has earned the highest government test ratings for durability, fire resistance, glue-holding ability, insulating properties, dimension stability, and termite resistance.

As if this were not enough—it already qualifies as the top-rated species in America—products of redwood are weather-resistant and require no paint or preservative treatment for protection. The wood is as shrinkproof as any species and the straightest-grained of its competitors.

At most of the forty redwood mills scattered from Port Orford, Oregon, down to Santa Cruz, the thick, stringy bark has been removed from the log before it is jack-laddered inside toward the saws. The white outer layer of sapwood glistens from its recent bath in the mill's log pond or from the water sprays used to remove saw-dulling dirt.

Greeted by the most powerful electric mill machinery in the world, the log is pushed, rolled, and flipped onto a wheeled carriage that rails it back and forth in front of the whirring band saw. A high-pitched screech accompanies the first cut, producing a curved slab that is rejected, at least for now, while the continuous belt of steel teeth bites on.

The man in charge of this primary step in the milling process is the head sawyer. At a glance, he must decide how best to cut the log as it whizzes by, his judgment worth hundreds of dollars a day in profit or loss.

As the log becomes squarer and smaller, the upper grades of reddish heartwood lumber appear, and with them, the main reason for redwood's durability and usefulness. The exposed wood has a soft, patinalike surface that seems to have a dimension of its own. This effect comes from an odd arrangement of cells. Hollow and thin-walled, they are often a hundred times as long as they are wide. Millions of such miscroscopic units combine to form fibers that are larger than those of most other trees. The result is light weight and an unsurpassed capacity to hold paint, stain, bleach, or glue.

The outsized fibers also account for redwood's weather resistance and ability to stop heat, cold, and sound. It means easier sawing too, whether in home workshop or mill.

After the headrig saw has completed slicing the log like a brick of cheese, the rough boards and planks move off on rollers to the edger and the second step in milling. Here each piece is sawed lengthwise into thinner strips of lumber.

As the moving wood continues to be reduced and refined, another of redwood's qualities shows up to further endear it to millmen: the lumber is free of pitch pockets, streaks, and resins.

To the builder, this means that redwood is as fire-resistant as softwood lumber can be. In a day before building codes, redwood pipe was sometimes used for fireplace chimneys in small houses of the region. It has even been used commercially as an electrical insulation material.

The greatest of testimonials came in 1906, when the disastrous fire following San Francisco's earthquake left many redwood structures standing untouched. On the spot, the mayor's emergency building committee ruled that no new construction would be permitted in the still-smoldering city unless it was of galvanized iron or redwood.

Some of the unique characteristics of "California cypress" had to be discovered from early use in Hawaii and the Spanish colonies, where lumber had been brought in before the Gold Rush. Under the punishing conditions of alternate rain and sunshine, redwood's durability proved much better than any other wood. Having built-in preservatives of phenol, cresol, and tannin, it repelled not only fungus and rot but also termites and other wood-chewing animal life of the tropics.

The men who manufactured redwood lumber were well aware of its many good qualities, but the rest of the world wasn't. Jepson observed that in the last century, the stuff "could scarcely be given away." Only a half century ago, it was selling in San Francisco for less than pine from the Sierra or fir from the Pacific Northwest.

The major manufacturers got together just before the opening of the 1915 Panama-Pacific Exposition and formed the California Redwood Association to promote their product. One of the organization's first projects was to prove redwood's virtues scientifically. It had to wait until the end of World War I, but by the mid-1920's results of the first comprehensive tests of the wood's properties and usefulness were being well publicized.

Technicians at the U.S. Department of Agriculture's Forest Products Laboratory found that redwood was moderately hard and stiff, having a good ability to hold nails. It did not warp or split. Tougher than Engelman spruce, red fir, eastern white pine, and red cedar, it was generally stronger than most of the western softwoods and topped a score of the nation's so-called hardwoods—chestnut, sweetgum, sycamore, and several types of maples and oaks among them. Nailed in place, it stayed put better than other species.

Because of even texture and straight grain, redwood received a high grade for workability—the ease of sawing, carving, sanding, or just plain whittling.

"It is decay-resistant even under conditions favoring decay," continued the official report card.

Government wood testers found that redwood shrinks or swells only two to three percent under extreme conditions, earning it another top competitive rating and making it a favorite for leak-free industrial tanks and vats. In cooling towers, CRA claims, it saves the nation billions of gallons of water each year.

Another plus in the industrial field comes from redwood's resistance to corrosives and chemicals. It is used by the manufacturers of glue, cheese, ink, whiskey, and soap. It helps process leather and pickles. It handles both acid and alkaline materials.

Then because the wood gives off no odor or flavor, it is specified by food processors, cigar-box makers, and brewers. Not only the premium wines of Northern California, but some of those of France are cured in redwood vats.

The many advantages of sempervirens as a product are not shared by its nearest relatives. The Sequoia of the Sierra was logged occasionally during the last century, but its lumber was found to be brashy and of low grade. The dawn redwood was tested recently at the U.S. Forest Products Laboratory and rated commercially valueless.

Tests have been of little use in demonstrating what may be redwood's best quality, durability. Only time can do that, and over the years the evidence has been coming in to prove that no one yet knows how long redwood will last.

"Virtually an everlasting wood," ventures the U.S. Department of Commerce.

The earliest applications were made at the time of America's Revolutionary War. Redwood was used in building such historical landmarks as the northern California missions, the Spanish presidios, General Vallejo's home, the Bale mill, Fort Humboldt, and the oldest all-wooden building west of the Rockies at Fort Ross. The homes of John Muir and Joaquin Miller, now California State Historic Sites, are among other survivors of the past. Most of these priceless treasures have come down to us today because they utilized redwood. Lesser building materials would have crumbled away long ago.

Impressed by its long life, a newspaper editor of the 1880's recommended wider use of redwood as a forest-conservation measure. He cited railroad ties as an example. By using California's red tree instead of other woods, the life expectancy of the ties was at least doubled, thus reducing the need for cutting trees by half.

The thought has proved to be a sound one, getting expanded treatment at a recent redwood national park hearing, where it was suggested that using more redwood products may be in the best interests of conservation. While the theme horrifies some preservationists, its justification is found in the remarkable productivity of the redwood forests. The wood products industry has long argued that the use of their renewable resource is a conservation measure, to be favored over the use of such materials as aluminum, concrete, steel, masonry, petroleum, and minerals, all of which are irreplaceable and disappearing treasures of the land. As long as American forests grow about as much timber as is being cut, the utilization of wood on a sustained-yield basis represents wise-use conservation. And because of redwood's speedy growth, the premise goes, it is what might be called the most renewable of all trees, so its total utilization could well represent the highest conservation goal.

Redwood products last so long that they are frequently used more than once. The Yolo causeway, built across flooding lowlands near Sacramento in the World War I era, was torn down recently and its redwood planks now decorate apartment houses in San Francisco. Timbers from old logging railroad trestles in Mendocino County have since found their way into many industrial, commercial, and residential buildings. The timbers salvaged by Captain John Sutter from Russian buildings at Fort Ross in 1841 went into the building of Sutter's fort. They are still there.

The early lumber products, hand-hewn with axes or crudely sawn, have their charm, but bear little resemblance to today's crisp-edged boards. Dimension redwood (of precise measurements) is formed by three separate sawing processes on the green, undried wood. The last of these is called trimming.

A nimble-fingered man called the trimmer sits alone in a compartment suspended above the mill floor where he can watch the fast-moving parade of edged lumber. His job is to trim off the ends of each piece to avoid knots and imperfections and to produce the most profitable lengths. This calls for a "catty" operator, who must make a quick decision, then pull two of a dozen levers that bring a pair of circular saws down across each board before it passes by.

Neatly rectangularized, the lumber ends its conveyor belt trip through the mill at the green chain. This is a roofed platform where each moving board is inspected for quality and marked by skilled graders, then removed and stacked. About ninety percent of all redwood products are graded under the supervision of the Redwood Inspection Service, an industry-wide organization of thirty-eight primary manufacturers.

Unlike most other types of lumber, the processing is not over for redwood. It contains a large amount of water in its freshly cut cells—more than any other commercial species—varying from sixty-five to three hundred percent of its dried weight. To reduce its water content, some of the green dimension gets an air-drying treatment in the vast rows of piled stacks that surround every redwood mill.

Even after a year, not all of the moisture has left the wood. So the better grades of lumber are placed in huge kilns for a week or two, where the water content is reduced to ten or twelve percent. The dehydrating process adds to the lumber's cost, but the Certified Kiln-Dried label assures users of a preshrunk, stress-free product.

The care required in redwood manufacturing prohibits the sudden fluctuations in production common throughout the rest of the lumber industry. As in the making of fine wine, there is only so much raw material available in a given year, with a limited capacity for processing. There's the further limitation of storage space in which to cure the product for a year or more before shipment.

After drying, some of the stock is further processed at the mill to become paneling, molding, shiplap, bevel siding, and fascia. Most of it goes into the familiar forms of house siding, joists, window frames, substructure, and beams. Two thirds of this year's production will be used in commercial, residential, farm, institutional, and industrial construction.

To most people, lumber means a board, though the term also embraces planks, timbers, beams, huge squares, and milled specialties. And here another redwood superlative appears: It can be milled by special order to the largest-sized, knot-free "board" of any wood. Among the king-size specimens is a twenty-one-foot-long plank, 6½ feet wide, on display at the University of California's Giannini Hall in Berkeley.

At the other extreme, small pieces of redwood under the

customary eight-foot length present no sales or disposal problems. In a score of states across the nation, remanufacturing plants use redwood to produce such items as ironing boards, saunas, incubators, doors, planter boxes, picnic tables, toys, and candy boxes.

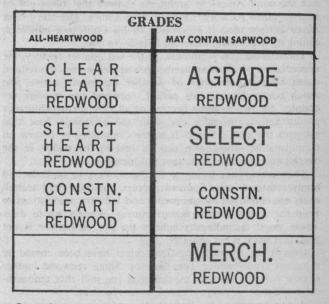

| GRADES | |
|---|---|
| **ALL-HEARTWOOD** | **MAY CONTAIN SAPWOOD** |
| CLEAR HEART REDWOOD | A GRADE REDWOOD |
| SELECT HEART REDWOOD | SELECT REDWOOD |
| CONSTN. HEART REDWOOD | CONSTN. REDWOOD |
| | MERCH. REDWOOD |

*Seven basic grades of lumber indicate redwood's variety and adaptability. A single mill may produce as many as forty-five designated grades.*

Even if redwood lacked the impressive collection of physical properties that make it the nation's most usable wood, modern science would be hard put to invent anything approaching its warmth and wide-ranging decorative beauty. There is nothing quite like it; no cypress, no cedar, no exotic tropical species. Heartwood, from the tree's lifeless core, varies in color from tan to dark mahogany. Sapwood, the outer living cylinder that sends nourishment up the tree's trunk, is a narrow band of creamy white.

There's almost everything that other woods offer somewhere in between. Stick up a redwood board on a fence, or a shingle on a roof, and it will gracefully weather over the years from red to tawny or dusty gray. The natural process can be stopped, teased, or accelerated by dozens of prepared finishes. Used for interior woodwork or paneling, the mystique of the forest seems to have been brought indoors.

A survey made by California Redwood Assocation among one thousand American architects showed that three out of four specified redwood for their own homes. The late Frank Lloyd Wright used it generously in his California buildings, calling it, "a beautiful material, friendly to man."

The friendship is reciprocal. In the last quarter century, the appreciation of redwood lumber has spread across the nation, aided by the popularity of another California native, the ranch house. During this period, redwood has steadily accounted for two to three percent of all U.S. softwood-lumber production. It provides one fifth the economic base that prompts the state's Forest Industry Committee to bestow on California its little-known title of first in the nation in the overall importance of its timber products complex.

They are always trying to find new ways to produce and apply redwood, with frequent success. Full-time staff technicians are employed by companies and industry associations to keep the state's earliest manufacturing industry up to date. These wood technologists believe the era of lumber is not past, that wood is not obsolete.

One of the recent innovations might have been envied by reluctant fence-painter Tom Sawyer. Some redwood lumber is now whizzed through machines at the mill that automatically add coats of paint, stain, or water repellent.

A new branch of the business that continues to grow is, to be more accurate, a revival of one started at least 140 years ago. The Russians again. In this case, the Fort Ross colonists were the first in America to prefabricate buildings. As early as 1827, they had shipped knockdown redwood houses to Alaska in the holds of sailing vessels. Today the big mills are producing precut vacation homes, patios, fencing, tool sheds, and swimming-pool frames.

Another first is claimed by a Southern California architect who has begun franchising factories across the country for the prefabricated building of what he calls redwood concept structures. These are twelve-foot-wide-modular living units up to sixty feet long, costing about twenty-five percent less than conventional buildings.

Then there's the company that recently developed an interlocking plank that, placed side by side, forms a complete house roof requiring no insulation, shingles, or finish material, top or bottom.

Redwood, product of a million centuries of natural adaptation, has adjusted well to Space Age needs. Its even-stress properties make it useful in testing rocket propellants, in building nose cones on dummy space missiles, and as shielding against radiation on nuclear-powered ships.

The CRA says there's no wood like redwood for many uses. It has no substitute in outdoor furniture, greenhouses, school buildings, stadium seats, corrosion-free pipelines, farm silos, caskets, highway dividers, bridges, and fences.

While redwood's characteristics are deserving of worldwide popularity, it raises the logical question of quality in raw-material supplies for the future.

By the end of this century, most of the timber harvested will be younger trees in the sixty- to one-hundred-year age classes. Assuming the timberland base remains available to keep the industry going at its present level of production, do the younger, smaller trees possess the same characteristics that have made old growth the most desirable of woods?

During World War II, when the armed forces used more tonnage of wood than steel, the commercial logging of second-crop redwoods began on a sizable scale. Young growth now accounts for nearly twenty percent of the industry's annual production. Even third-growth trees are being cut in some forests first logged in Spanish and Russian colonial days.

The quality of this wood is the subject of continuing studies made by the U.S. Forest Products Laboratory, CRA, Humboldt State College, and the California Forest Products Laboratory. They show that, yes, there will be wider-spaced growth rings in wood from selectively logged forests, but only for the tree's first half century or until branches of the forest canopy close in and slow its growth. Wood from a clear-cut logging operation loses its wide rings earlier because the young trees compete with each other in uniform growth rates.

The sapwood grows no thicker—about two inches inside the bark—than on old trees. Young heartwood is equally resistant to insects and fungi.

The lumber companies report neither milling nor drying problems in processing logs from younger trees.

The most important findings have been that in dimensional stability, stiffness, strength, and low-shrinkage properties, young growth will generally meet present standards for old growth and in shear strength (tension perpendicular to the grain) and screw-holding ability exceeds them. Wood from young trees becomes more like old growth with age. So the key to future utilization of young growth lies in what products will be made of it.

Many of the qualities that make redwood so desirable are inherent in the species, CRA explains. Unlike other commercial trees, most young redwoods have grown from stump sprouts and will possess almost the exact traits of their parents. Redwood, it seems, is redwood.

Perhaps the greatest advantage of young growth is its lack of defect, the punky heartwood in overmature trees caused by a fungus disease that enters through old fire scars. While disease has never been known to kill a standing tree, it is responsible for an average of thirty percent of unusable wood. Fire has now been controlled and the fungus is rare. So the special Humboldt scale for measuring the board-foot volume of old growth is waived, increasing the volume measure of young growth by nearly one half.

Yet the increase is deceptive. No matter how you slice it, only about two thirds of the log that entered the mill can be manufactured into dimension lumber. With some five thousand different products now being made from wood, there is a question whether such unsophisticated examples as boards and beams will dominate redwood's future. There has been a trend toward a specialty wood in recent years, not because of cost or imagined scarcity but because of its qualities, which can be matched by no other species.

The redwood people say this makes it imperative—from both the conservation and economic standpoints—to convert all the available wood volume to its highest use. The realization has taken longer in the Redwood Region than other areas, due mainly to the difficulty of understanding the wood's unusual makeup. And that in turn explains another reason why you can't invent the redwood, at least with today's knowledge. But one by one, the secrets are being found—and with them, more surprises.

## Chapter VII

## *The Tree·Stretchers*

•

To most Americans, conservation of the redwoods has come to mean consignment of forested areas to park or wilderness status, untouched, inviolate. This is a worthwhile and essential effort for a tree of such outstanding scenic beauty, but it is better described by the term "preservation." It is only one of the elements contributing to the objectives of conservation, which since Teddy Roosevelt's day has been universally defined as wise use of our natural resources.

What we do with what we have is the measure. And in the redwoods, conservationists—whether practicing or theoretical—can find heart-warming progress in the history of man's concern for nature's useful gifts.

Without cutting one additional tree, the people who manufacture redwood products in the last decade have learned how to squeeze more than twice as much usable material out of each board foot of fiber. This type of wise use, based on the reduction of waste, has the same effect as making our commercial forests twice as large. If conservation of the forests is important, so too is conservation at the mill.

Leftovers from the wasteful process of making rectangular boards out of round logs were formerly burned. Now look what they're doing with odd bits and pieces of the tree with a one hundred-million-year past:

Redwood fibers have been put to work filtering sewage, tanning leather, and growing orchids. They help produce better playgrounds, vegetable gardens, and golf courses. They can be transformed into glue, paper towels, oil filters, and mackinaw jackets. A popular breath-sweetner is made from what its manufacturer calls "redwood juice."

Hundreds of new products and uses have been developed under the heading of utilization. By-products, they used to be called. Conservation values aside, the promising growth of utilization has sprouted from economic roots. When the value of standing timber began to rise after World War II, it soon became too expensive to waste wood fibers. More "mileage" from the tree became a financial necessity.

The original redwood products of shakes, shingles, posts, and grape stakes offer an example. These are still hand-manufactured in the woods with simple tools, but the "split products men" now make them from parts of logs and the old high stumps left behind from early logging operations. It is a conservation move dictated in part by the economic fact that complete logs are now more valuable for lumber products.

One of the earliest steps toward utilization may have been caused more by necessity than by inspiration. Stringy and tough, redwood bark has always had to be removed from the log because it causes mill saws to wobble and quickly dulls their cutting edge. Growing as much as a foot thick, making up nearly one fifth of the volume of each tree, and being fire-resistant, it presented a dirty, expensive disposal problem.

Someone decided to chop the stuff up, and a new by-products industry was born. Bark, it was found, made a decorative ground cover for patios and gardens; a springy carpet on playgrounds, athletic fields, and horse tracks; and an insulating material for homes, industrial buildings, and refrigerators.

Being uniquely vermin-resistant, the durable fibers found value as floor litter in commercial poultry-growing houses.

Sandwiched between two pieces of heavy paper, there is no better cushion for fruit packing and shipping.

On a volume basis, the most popular use of redwood bark is as a garden compost and soil conditioner. It softens the earth, provides better aeration, and is both weed- and salt-free.

Until about a quarter century ago, all bark was removed in the woods by men called peelers, who used muscle power and the spud, a long, chisel-headed crowbar, to rip it off the log.

Then came the mechanical barker, which strips the logs by

friction. Some mills use wedge-bladed air hammers or tractors equipped with pronged blades to separate the bark.

The most effective method is by hydraulic jet. Visitors at larger lumber mills stand fascinated behind bullet-proof windows as they watch spinning logs stripped by water sprayed at pressures of 1,300 pounds to the square inch.

Passing out of the lumber mill on a conveyor belt, the bark is then ground or shredded for uses undreamed of only a few decades ago. Experimentally in some cases, it has been successfully applied to the manufacture of bed blankets, ceramic ware, lead-acid batteries, roofing felt, detergents, and mattresses. In industry, it has been used for ore flotation, seed cleaning, oil-well drilling, and as a grinding aid.

From orchid-potting medium to industrial boiler cleaning, bark has become a Cinderella material of many uses. Others are coming. Chemicals and tannins, which give the bark its reddish color, have been successfully extracted. Recent tests have shown that redwood bark, being one of the few natural cellulose fibers that is both durable and harmless to aquatic organisms, works well as a trickling filter in sewage-treatment plants.

Then there's the perennial waste problem that earned for lumber mills everywhere the name of sawdust factories. It remains a problem for many of the West's pine and fir mills, but sawdust from redwood-lumber manufacture has been converted to profit as a long-lasting soil additive, widely used by commercial flower and vegetable growers.

Restructuring the tree by gluing thin veneers of redwood into the wooden sandwich called plywood was first tried in 1890 without success. When the first Douglas fir plywood appeared in 1905, it was tried again. Unsuccessful experiments continued in 1926 and the 1930's. The frustrations came mainly from inadequate glues and the tendency of redwood to develop huge ray or rift cracks when drying out. Then it was discovered that a redwood log, unlike others, must be steamed before it can be peeled on a lathe. Staple-like metal or plastic dogs were developed to prevent splitting of the log. And following the introduction of new glues in the 1940's, someone added the final touch for success—the perfection of alloyed knife blades resistant to redwood chemicals.

This year, four companies will produce about sixty-five million square feet of the decorative panels, or enough for a train of three thousand boxcars. All of it is manufactured with waterproof glues, making it usable indoors or out. Some are made with inside layers of fir as a further help in stretching the supply of redwood.

The new types of glue brought another bonus in conservation at mills throughout the nation by making possible a new by-products industry—the manufacture of big pieces of lumber out of little ones.

"We make it by the mile and cut it off by the yard," says Russell Ells of Willits Redwood Products Co. He is describing the process called end-gluing, in which odd pieces of board are finger-jointed at each end, then glued, and under electronic heat and pressure formed into endless strips.

Glue the small pieces of milling leftovers side by side and they can be made as wide as needed. Then with a combination of end- and edge-gluing, three redwood companies produce large panels having several types of natural textures or surface finishes applied at the mill. The product is welcomed in commercial and home building, and fills industrial needs for outsized units, such as boxcar lining.

Union Lumber Co. has been the pioneer in utilizing small blocks and pieces. "We tried gluing anything that didn't walk away," recalls Dr. N. V. Poletika, head of redwood research and development. One of the results is the first laminated beam to be made of redwood, a product considered to be more handsome than the solid length of wood it replaces. Glu-lam is available in numerous shapes and lengths up to fifty feet, making it a favorite of architects for churches and large buildings.

In common with other engineered wood products, the many parts glued together offer an appealing showcase for all the varied moods of redwood color and grain. And in gluing, these boards, panels, and beams become stronger than the sum of their parts.

The drive toward total utilization has been hard on the tepees, those ugly, round waste burners that, like red-glowing lighthouses, once marked every lumber mill in the country.

In the redwoods, tepees are following their Indian namesake into oblivion. Under the new economics of utilization, they were found to be burning money. A few are still aglow, usually at remote locations. Several mills burn some of their scraps to generate steam for heating the dry kilns, power for running plant machinery, and sometimes to provide standby electric power for local communities. For the most part, the only redwood burned today is in the popular fireplace fuel called a Pres-to-Log. And it's made of shavings swept from the planning mill floor.

Mill waste first became valuable twenty years ago when Masonite Corp. at Ukiah pioneered the manufacture of redwood hardboard, the tough four-by-eight-foot panels of many uses.

A totally new type of board for building purposes has been perfected by Miller Redwood Co. after years of research and development. The inch-thick material is formed entirely of mechanically ground redwood fibers and is rated stronger and lighter than conventional hardboard.

Then there's particle board, made of various-sized chips, shavings, and even sawdust. Like the other panels, it is formed in huge presses. It is available in its natural reddish color or prepainted.

But most of the slabs, edgings, and trimmings left over from basic lumber processing go to the chipper, a noisy machine that chops and slices odd pieces into thin flakes uniformly about one inch long.

Some redwood chips are sold for making composition roofing material, molded wood products, and plastic wood.

Above all, chips are the stuff of pulp and paper manufacturing, and so far, this use has marked the greatest advance in milling conservation in the redwoods.

A survey made by Emanuel Fritz forty-five years ago showed that as much as one hundred million board feet of redwood was being wasted each year in forest and mills. There wasn't much improvement by 1961, when Deputy State Forester Tobe Arvola reported enough unused wood leftovers in the Redwood Region to increase California's production of pulp more than fivefold.

Tests made by the Institute of Paper Chemistry, the U.S. Forest Products Laboratory, and company technicians showed that redwood pulp could produce a long-fibered paper with excellent strength qualities. But it took many years to conquer the technical problems caused by redwood's strange chemical makeup and to secure a dependable source of water for the mills.

By 1965, a process using about half Douglas fir and half redwood chips was perfected and the first mill was built by Georgia-Pacific Corp. at Samoa, across the bay from Eureka.

Simpson Timber Co. teamed with the pioneer Crown Zellerbach Corp. and a year later built a similar bleached kraft pulp mill a mile away at Fairhaven. The mills of G-P and Crown Simpson Pulp Co. each has a capacity of over five hundred tons a day and together cost more than eighty million dollars.

The people of the pulp mill firms had many years of experience behind them at other company plants and were able to incorporate the latest effluent recovery devices as a means of protecting fish life. They were aided by the improved sulfate or kraft process, which unlike others, recovers the chemicals for cooking wood chips and uses them over and over. Fisheries expert Dr. James A. Gast of Humboldt State College assists company technicians in making regular tests of outfall water quality. They have found none of the symptoms of industrial waste pollution that plagued some earlier pulp mills.

Around the world, such mills often have an eye-irritating, nose-wrinkling way of making their presence known. But records show the Humboldt Bay pulp factories have actually helped clean up the atmosphere.

Aiming for cleaner skies from the beginning, the builders took advantage of recent technological breakthroughs and have spent about four million dollars in air quality-control devices, including a complete weather station atop the roof of one plant. Significantly, Simpson itself is a major manufacturer of so-called air scrubbers, a type of pollution-checking equipment.

The cleanup was indirect. It came when many of the area's lumber mill tepees stopped burning leftover wood. Prior to 1966, Eurekans resignedly bore the burden of a typical mill town and watched fly ash drop from the skies at the rate of as much as one ton to the square mile each day. The pulp mills' appetite for wood chips gradually began to be felt until by 1968 the monitoring program was canceled because fallout was not enough to bother measuring.

Since no whole logs are used in pulping, the lumber-milling operations of the parent companies contribute their chips. But this isn't enough. Sixty small redwood and whitewood firms of the region have either installed their own chippers or send their leftovers to central chipping points. The two Eureka pulp mills receive chips by rail and truck from lumber mills as far as two hundred miles away.

The new industry has created an annual payroll of about

six million dollars, pays $1.4 million in local taxes and provides five or six hundred jobs directly plus hundreds more indirectly. Unlike logging, fisheries, and tourism, this is a year-round bonus to the area's economy.

Now that the once-wasted fibers of redwood milling are going into such products as paper toweling, tissues, grocery bags, wax paper, and writing bond, the processors are looking to the future. Each American is using an average of 540 pounds of paper products a year, a rate that continues to rise. From redwood chips we may soon be getting filter papers, food container board, and disposable paper clothing.

The benefits of waste utilization have been felt in the forest, too. "We've got the biggest scrounging operation I've seen since the Army," says one of the woodsmen engaged in what is called relogging. Because there's now an economic use for them, low grade and damaged logs of several species are worth pulling out of the woods. Small rubber-tired tractors are sent into previously logged areas to salvage any logs or pieces that may have been left behind—a year ago or thirty years ago.

The utilization explosion has also made it possible to manufacture products out of the small logs called pee-wees. This in turn permits the economic thinning of thick stands of young redwoods to speed up the overall growth rate of the forest.

The nationwide trend toward conversion of the log has doomed many of the smaller, uneconomic lumber mills. Unable to produce anything but boards and two-by-fours, the nonintegrated "peckerwood" plants are succumbing to rising costs of raw material, production, and distribution.

It's dramatically evident in the redwoods, where the utilization breakthroughs came suddenly and within a decade helped reduce the number of mills by half.

Overall, the loss is not serious. Employment is averaged out by the increased man-hours per board foot it takes to produce more refined products. The surviving mills, with assured timber supplies and adequate financing, are getting the highest-possible returns from the log and constantly improving their products to meet progressive market conditions. Some companies now offer more than fifty different products in their redwood line.

They have only begun to unwrap the tree. Just six decades ago the first wood-research laboratory in the world was established by the U.S. Department of Agriculture at Madison, Wisconsin. In partnership with the Forest Service's Pacific Southwest Forest and Range Experiment Station at Berkeley, it has played a leading role in the conservation and intensified utilization of redwood.

The University of California opened a Forest Products Laboratory at Richmond in 1955 and has devoted much of its work to the state's unique tree.

These government efforts are backed up by product research done at UC's School of Forestry and Conservation and Humboldt State College. Several of the redwood companies maintain their own research and development staffs. This work in turn is often coordinated through the technical committees formed by the California Redwood Association, the Forest Products Research Society, and the National Forest Products Association.

While the foresters try to grow more wood faster, the product researchers apply their scientific knowledge to serve society with the most useful returns from the available trees. These are the men who have converted once-wasted wood into products instead of problems.

The wood wizards have uncovered some exciting prospects. Chemotaxonomy, the identification of wood's chemical makeup, by itself has recently opened up an entire new field of exploration. One specialist, Dr. Arthur B. Anderson of the Richmond laboratory, calls a tree "the most marvelous chemical factory in existence." And while more than 2,600 different organic chemicals have so far been identified in the world's trees, the primitive redwood still holds many secrets.

Only in recent years was it learned how to remove redwood's natural preservatives of phenol and cresol on a commercial basis. A professor at the Swedish Royal Institute of Technology suspects that these chemicals, which along with tannin contribute to the redwood's great size and age, may provide a key to longer life-spans for humans. In 1968, a method was found to produce myo-inositol, a member of the vitamin B complex, from redwood residues. Redwood bark extract is one of the promising materials being tested for possible use in treating human cancer. At least a dozen other projects are under way to find ways to increase the total benefits people get from the redwood forests.

In the last century, only one third of the redwood tree could be made into lumber having a market value. The remainder was left in the woods or otherwise wasted. Now the useful portion of the tree has risen to seventy-five percent and is still climbing.

"They don't leave enough of the tree out in the woods these days to make a woodpecker's lunch," says an old logger.

An economic study by Dean John A. Zivnuska of UC's School of Forestry and Conservation shows that the North Coast in the next decade will be making use of about twenty-five percent more wood from the same amount of trees now being cut.

No one cares to predict what directions tomorrow's utilization will take. As a raw material, wood may have more uses now and greater future possibilities than any other.

The hope might be realized in undiscovered chemicals. Or machinery could be developed that will pick up branches, tops, needles, and slash left from logging and grind it into some useful material. Mysterious lignin may someday prove as valuable as the wood fibers it holds together. Bark, sawdust, and more sophisticated uses of lumber also show promise. Eventually it will probably be a combination of all the possibilities—spurred by a demand for wood products expected to double in the next thirty years—that will bring redwood to its full potential.

The new by-products themselves have generated other by-products for the region. These include new jobs, tax revenues, a more stable year-round economy, and improved use of our resources. Perhaps most important of the benefits is something the textbooks refer to as a link in the economic chain of forestry: the overlooked fact that upgrading the redwood's board-foot value has provided the income necessary to finance better management practices out in the forest.

## Chapter VIII

# *The Fern Hoppers*

Scientific forestry, the partnership of man and nature in growing trees, is younger in the redwoods than the age of most of the professionals who practice it.

Through the first century and a half of logging, there were a number of good reasons to believe that forest management might never arrive. It was costly and a nuisance. No one knew or cared about the quality of lumber the new crop of trees might produce.

The profession of forestry was untried and unappreciated. Textbooks mentioned the redwood only in passing. When the college graduates slowly began to infiltrate the woods, disapproving loggers usually called them scenery inspectors or fern hoppers—when they were called anything printable. Their professional advice turned out to be bad as often as it was good.

As for the first principle of forestry—protection of the standing trees—well, that's not necessary here, is it? After all, said the practical lumbermen, there are some kind of chemicals in redwood bark and fibers that make the tree fireproof, insect-proof, and disease-proof.

Besides, consoled the leading lumber trade journal of 1900, "There is enough redwood to last for many hundreds of years at the present rate of cutting."

In the classic pattern of centuries of American history, logging was essentially a land-clearing operation, a taming of the wilderness, and the sooner the trees made way for agriculture, the better. "It is the natural sequence that the plow should follow the axe," said a Pacific Logging Congress speaker in 1914. The U.S. Department of Agriculture officially advised lumbermen to plant forage crops on logged-off land; it would reduce the fire hazard.

Union Lumber Co. was among the progressive redwood companies that took the best scientific advice of the day and replanted cutover land near the "Skunk Line" railroad with eucalyptus, apple, and walnut trees.

The primitive state of forestry in the years preceding World War I was indicated by the response the U.S. Forest Service received from a questionnaire sent to the lumber industry. When asked "What provision do you make for reproduction?" nearly all operators left a blank. Among the few who responded, one commented that "nothing of the kind is allowed in my camps!"

But the early forest managers realized they had a dream tree to work with. Redwood dominates all other species of plants on its native soil and is a primary invader on the land growing other trees. Its home territory represents about a quarter of California's highest site, or best tree-growing land.

As for natural regeneration, there's no other useful tree as dependably prolific and tenacious. It not only regrows from seeds, in common with most other plants, but sends up new trees by sprouting from trunk, stump, or roots. Fallen trees have been known to grow healthy youngsters from old limbs. Even the large gray squirrel of the region has helped plant new trees by cutting down cones in the fall, burying them, and then forgetting where.

If man wants to help nature, there are three methods of artificial reforestation. Collected seeds can be sown on the bare ground. Seedling trees, a year or two old, can be hand-planted by digging a hole and tamping them in. Even cut branches and twigs will grow when stuck in the ground, though this is an uncommon and unreliable practice. Old-time Hoopa Indians have passed on the legend explaining the strange grove of redwoods growing on their reservation twenty miles east of the tree's natural range. It was caused, they say, by an absentminded ancestor who, en route from the coast, stuck his redwood walking stick in the ground while resting and journeyed on without it.

The obvious potential of the reseeding process was noted by UC botanist Willis L. Jepson when he walked through a tract in Mendocino County that had been logged forty years earlier. A few trees had been left behind because they were too large to handle or were not considered worth hauling to the mill. The seeds they dropped had become trees that quickly filled in all the gaps in the forest.

## CROSS SECTION OF A REDWOOD TRUNK

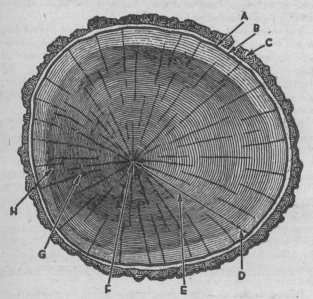

A-CAMBIUM  C-OUTER BARK  E-HEARTWOOD  G-RAY
B-INNER BARK  D-SAPWOOD  F-PITH  H-ANNUAL RINGS

Dr. Jepson realized that by applying elementary forestry principles, land in the Redwood Region could be the most productive in the country. He became the first prophet of redwood forestry in the 1890's, when he persuaded the owners of Mendocino Lumber Co. to leave uncut all the trees smaller than twenty inches thick as a source of seeds for the future forest.

It was found that the "leave trees" can begin dropping seeds when they are mere saplings, though it generally takes at least twenty years before the tree bears a fair crop.

The early gropings toward proper land management were helped in 1903, when several redwood lumbermen called on the new U.S. Bureau of Forestry for advice. The profession of forestry in America was then only ten years old, but the results of the government's six-month study turned up the first scientific evidence that redwood could become a crop tree.

Few improvements in the forestry situation took place in the next decade, though several redwood lumbermen got together in 1912 to launch an ill-fated tree-planting program.

It was a time when *West Coast Lumberman* magazine was telling its readers that "the great opportunity in logged-off land is found in dairying, cattle and hog-raising because it does not require the removal of stumps." But Jepson and leaders of the timber industry were now campaigning for establishment of a school of forestry on UC's Berkeley campus. Success came in 1915. Things would never be the same in the redwoods.

One of the first of the university's new breed was a slender, brown-shocked young forestry professor, fresh from World War I duty as a U.S. Army Air Service officer, who decided to do something to help realize the region's untapped forest-management potential. His name was Emanuel Fritz, now better known as Mr. Redwood. An iron jaw and menacing eyebrows, combined with the dozen cigars he chewed up every day, would prove helpful props in the big job ahead.

With soft-spoken logic or fiery-eyed invective that could terrorize his students, the respected professor had the rare ability to persuade tough loggers or tough company presidents to do the right thing. Today in his eighties, he still does.

What was needed, Fritz believed, was a dramatic demonstration on the ground to convince the lumbermen that their cutover land had a future, that redwood land was the bank account and trees the interest. In 1922, Fritz and Professor Woodbridge Metcalf selected a one-acre piece of forest land on the south bank of Mendocino County's Big River and induced the owners to commit it to a permanent sample plot.

The area had been logged with bull team in 1858. Only five trees had been left behind. But their seeds, in combination with sprouts from stumps, had produced a thick forest of sixty-year-old trees as tall as a seventeen-story building.

Fritz was able to show that the trees had grown an average of 2,100 board feet each year, which to a lumberman then meant a value of perhaps fifty to seventy-five dollars. Over

# Eternal Redwood
## Forests

The magnificent climax redwood groves in California's redwood parks, one of which is shown on the cover of this book, are known throughout the world. To most people, these inspiring stands seem eternal and are revered as such. However, in reality, these groves, viewed in historical perspective, may be doomed. The largest trees, already at a terminal growth stage, number their future years at most in the hundreds; many will fall long before then. Storms, floods, old age, topheaviness take their inescapable toll.

But the redwood forests themselves are truly everlasting. Nature has endowed these extraordinary trees with a unique and remarkable regenerative ability. Largely through sprouts from the root systems of fallen trees, and also through reseeding from surrounding trees, young redwoods rapidly replace their venerable predecessors. Aided by modern forestry practices, vast new forests today cover areas that once seemed to be denuded.

The following four pages picture the remarkable regrowth ability of redwood forests. Given proper soil and moisture conditions, with adequate air and sunshine, the redwood is the fastest growing of all American conifers.

*First color photo:* In an area logged by settlers a little over a hundred years ago, Nature has regenerated giant trees. Some of these "new" redwoods near Fort Bragg, California, are now more than two hundred feet tall and twenty feet in girth.

*Second color photo:* Nature fills in the redwood forest rapidly behind man's chainsaws and tractors. Over sixty percent of the timber volume has been removed from this commercial forest area by singling out the oldest and damaged trees for removal. Accelerated growth of the remaining trees, as well as new trees from stump sprouts and seedlings, will replace in less than forty years the volume of timber removed.

*Third color photo:* A sylvan fishing spot typifies the scenic beauty and recreation opportunity which abound amid commercial redwood forests. Lumber companies have opened hundreds of thousands of acres of such privately owned lands to the public for recreational use.

*Color photo opposite:* A vista destined to be truly everlasting. All of these redwood forest lands, stretching as far as the eye can see, were "laid barren" by older logging methods; yet, through the marvelous reproductive gift of *Sequoia sempervirens,* vast new forests have been regenerated. In fact, under proper forestry practices, such lands seem able to nurture and support commercially producing redwood forests for an indefinite period.

the years, continuing measurements showed that Fritz' "Wonder Plot" could produce enough wood every four years to build a house. Today this single acre of cutover contains a total of more than a quarter million feet, which is well above the average found in virgin forests.

The professor's lesson was not lost on C. R. Johnson, whose Union Lumber Co. owned land on the other side of the river. In 1922, his firm became the first in the redwoods to declare a policy of managing timber for perpetual production.

Major David T. Mason, recently of the UC faculty, was hired as a consultant by a group of six redwood companies to find out if permanent forest management would pay. It would, he concluded after a year's full-time study. Further, by growing crops of trees like crops of corn, there would be economic stability for company employees and people of the local communities.

The influence of a decade of forestry at the university was now felt in the field. Professor Donald Bruce contributed growth studies. Professor Metcalf came up with pros and cons on tree nurseries. Professor Warren T. Clarke created quite a stir; his research showed that it would be more economical to regrow trees on cutover land than to convert to agriculture.

There was still some foot dragging by hard-to-convince lumbermen who believed that young redwood trees produced an inferior grade of lumber, making regrowth forests not worth cultivating. In 1923, Fritz had a sample of sixty-five-year-old trees logged and run through a mill. No boards were ever as closely examined and tested.

The verdict was favorable. The young trees had produced a salable product, offering for the first time dollar-sign proof that the next crop could pay its way.

The evidence convinced the principals of seven other companies, who followed Union's lead in opting for permanent production. In a half-dozen years, the university's forestry salesmen had sold their product to the men who then manufactured eighty-six percent of all redwood lumber. The business of growing trees was now part of the business of making boards.

Another of the pioneer foresters' accomplishments was in controlling man-caused wildfires. The dangers had been recognized as early as 1744, when the Spanish government decreed California's first law prohibiting the deliberate setting of fires. It had been conveniently ignored by rancheros, Indians, missionaries, colonial officials, and nearly all who followed them.

Widespread burning was an old California custom to clear the land for livestock grazing and to maintain forage. Woodsmen commonly burned the forest both before and after logging. Shepherds reportedly built large and uncontrolled fires around their herds to keep predatory animals away. Campers and hunters often let their campfires escape. Old-timers reported the timbered area of Mendocino County had been swept by fast-moving blazes about every five or ten years for half a century.

Most of these fires passed harmlessly through the old redwoods, protected by a moist habitat, asbestoslike bark, water-filled cells, and lower limbs one hundred or two hundred feet above the ground. As long as the moisture- and nutrient-carrying sapwood was not girdled, the trees grew on. When severe fires hit, about the worst that happened was the burning out of an area in the trunk that permitted a nonfatal fungus disease, *poria sequioae*, to enter and begin a very slow deterioration of the heartwood.

Young redwoods are different. For their first one hundred years, needles on lower branches are susceptible to fatal scorching by the rising heat of a surface fire. And it takes about twenty years or more for their bark to develop the fire-resistant qualities of mature trees. Until then they will burn as readily as the neighboring fir, pine, spruce, and hardwood trees.

After the turn of the century the forests became increasingly valuable. Large investments were made in mills and land. If the lumber industry was sincere in its plans for perpetual forests, then the waste of fire must be stopped to protect tomorrow's trees.

The big move came in the 1920's, just after passage of the Clarke-McNary Act offering federal encouragement in fire protection. The major redwood operators, competing businessmen all, got together with government landowning agencies of the region to form the state's first cooperative fire-defense program. The agreement made between members of California Redwood Association and the State Board of Forestry nearly fifty years ago set a pattern of fire control that is still in effect.

Mutual-assistance pacts were made among landowners. Patrol roads were built and fire wardens hired. Logging crews found themselves equipped with fire-fighting tools. It was a move typical of the frontier character of the region, undertaken in a time when all the West's forest-fire-protection laws were weak and poorly enforced.

It was obvious to Fritz and other forestry evangelists that their programs for continous crops of trees would always be endangered by fire. They preached fire control to ranchers, loggers, and hunters who were reared on the belief that fire is harmless in the redwoods. It might even be good for the forest. "That is sheer nonsense," growled the professor. Costly, devastating fires that struck the region in 1923, 1936, and 1945 lent tragic emphasis.

Today the system of fire protection in the redwoods is as good as that in any forest. There have been no major fires for a quarter of a century.

The State Division of Forestry has primary fire-protection responsibility. Their lonely watchers in the hilltop lookout towers are aided by a mobile radio system linking private foresters, logging foremen, company officers, patrolmen, and government forest rangers.

In 1948, the region claimed another first when it sent aloft the state's pioneer aerial fire-detection patrol. Flying an average of six hundred summertime hours a year, the two-plane redwood air force has been responsible for discovering and reporting forty percent of the fires started while the craft were in the air. Landowners pay 1.5¢ an acre each year for their now-indispensable eye in the sky, and the Division of Forestry cooperates by providing radio communications and assigning patrolmen.

The stubborn fern hoppers were more successful than they hoped in establishing fire protection and a new conservation awareness in the redwoods. Now there were other measures —good and bad—that had to be tried out along the bumpy trail to well-managed forests.

Prompt reforestation, the restocking of cutover land to its full capacity of new trees, has always been a problem someplace. Parts of the forest fail to spring back to new green life for a number of reasons. It might have been careless early logging practices, fires among the vulnerable young trees, a poor seed year, drought, wind, unsuccessful conversion of forest land to agriculture, repeated damage from tree-nibbling rodents and deer or the browsing of flocks of sheep that also trampled the ground so that seeds could not germinate.

These were man-caused shortcomings. Nature had been performing the miracle of regeneration by seeds for a hundred million years. Each winter, male flowers release a sulphur-colored pollen that falls in great breeze-blown clouds across the female flower buds. Ten months later, the pollinated bud has become a cone and releases its seeds—tiny specks of eternity that weigh 120,000 to the pound.

Here was an unequaled bounty of potential trees, a shower of seeds ranging as high as half a billion to the acre. It would be simple to imitate this particular means of natural reproduction and, better yet, do it the way reforestation was accomplished elsewhere: by planting seeds in nurseries, then transplanting only the thriving young seedlings to the forest. Logically, this became the basis of the first shaky attempts to realize the promise of the redwoods.

The lumber business was good in the 1920's and redwood operators, listening now to what the foresters had to say, made a typically bold move. With all-out encouragement from the Save-the-Redwoods League, fourteen lumber companies and the University of California incorporated the Redwood Reforestation Association and embarked on the nation's first cooperative forest-planting program. One of forestry's splendid failures was in the making.

Enthusiastically, the project began with establishment of the state's first private forest nursery at Fort Bragg in 1922. Three other nurseries were soon added and began turning out a million seedlings a year for members of the association.

Forester A. M. Corbitt of The Pacific Lumber Co. offered encouragement. In the program's first year, he had gathered cones holding five million seeds from a single tree.

Troubles appeared at the beginning. Though coast redwood produces a good crop of seeds almost every year, they are relatively low in viability, the capacity to take root and grow. U.S. Forest Service studies have since shown that successful seed germination ranges from a low of one percent to a high of thirty-six percent. The dozen foresters working with the association at the time figured germination would be from twenty to forty percent.

Out in the field, where crews of men laboriously hand-planted the foot-high trees, it became evident that seedling survival would also be low. The discouraging reports from three counties piled up. In spite of careful planting on selected sites, only one in five transplants was alive in 1929. Others would die later, primarily from lack of moisture. Less than four percent survival from seed to tree was not good forestry and certainly not good business.

Wildfires and animals damaged some of the planted acreage, and the Depression of the 1930's dampened whatever hope was left. Even the range grass and eucalyptus and fruit trees hopefully planted earlier had all but disappeared.

In the midst of the noble experiment, Dr. W. C. Cannon

## WOODS WORDS

ALLOWABLE CUT—the amount of timber that may be harvested each year from a managed forest to maintain a balance with growth.

MATURE—a tree that has reached its maximum growth before declining. Economic maturity is the age or size at which harvest is advisable. Physiological maturity, when the redwood possesses all the characteristics of the species including reproductive potential, occurs at about twenty-five years.

MULTIPLE USE—management of forest land to produce not only timber, but also, where possible, benefits such as recreation, fishlife, wildlife, and livestock grazing.

OLD GROWTH—a stand of timber having seventy percent or more mature trees. Most "old" redwood trees are less than five hundred years of age, according to the Society of American Foresters.

SEED TREES—the timber left standing after logging to assure natural reseeding as a supplement to stump sprouting; also residuals, leave trees.

SUSTAINED YIELD—forest management that produces a supply of timber equal to the amount cut on a perpetual basis.

TREE FARM—a privately owned, taxpaying, commercial forest of ten acres or larger where the certified owner has pledged to grow continuous crops and to protect the trees from fire, insects, and disease.

VIRGIN FOREST—a stand of timber unaffected by human activity. Purists insist that all redwood forests have been modified to some extent by such things as fires set by Indians and early settlers, wildlife imbalance, smog, and livestock grazing.

YOUNG GROWTH—a stand of timber having less than thirty percent mature (old-growth) trees.

conducted a study of root regeneration, financed by the Save-the-Redwoods League. It showed that neither fire, flood, drought, nor logging killed the roots of the redwood, which continued to grow and send up the sprouts of new trees. No one paid much attention.

In 1929, the University's Dr. Elmer D. Merrill issued a report stating flatly that "reforestation by planting in the Redwood Region is wrong." The Reforestation Association was dissolved the next year.

The effort had cost the lumbermen a quarter of a million dollars, or about twelve dollars for each acre planted. Money, enthusiasm, and the best forestry knowledge of the time had failed, but a useful scientific lesson about the way of the redwoods had been learned.

# Chapter IX

## *The Eternal Redwood*

Visitors to the Redwood Empire often return home with living samples of the phenomenon that has allowed sempervirens to survive the eons where other plants have failed. These are the bumpy, brownish pieces of wood called burls. Place one in a dish of water, and it will soon send up the lacy green foliage of a new tree.

The souvenir burl is a growth oddity that might be likened to living scar tissue, formed of a mass of buds grown on the redwood's trunk in response to some outside injury, such as a blow from a falling tree. But formations of buds in burl clusters are rare. Similar buds also grow normally under the bark of all redwood trees, dormant, waiting to be released. It is a means of reproduction one scientist has called "the immortal protoplasm."

At the age of six months, it has been found, seedlings begin to develop a collar of burls at the ground line. These are capable of sending up new sprouts should their tops be taken off by frost, drought, fire, or grazing animals.

It takes a disturbance of some kind to stimulate the buds to grow into twigs. They may appear as soon as three weeks after a redwood has been cut, burned, toppled by wind or flood, received silt or rocks around its base, or otherwise damaged on its trunk. Even cut logs floating in the lumber mill pond sometimes sprout. The people at The Pacific Lumber Company were not too surprised to find that the rough-barked logs used as rustic columns in their brand new Scotia bank building were growing branches even though the trees had been cut several months earlier.

Within twenty-four months after logging, a Division of Forestry study shows, nine out of ten logged stumps have sprouted. Where one tree stood before, there may now be dozens of young trees growing from its stump, though the average has been thinned down to fourteen after five years. Some eager suckers reach twelve feet in height in one season's growth.

These are tough youngsters. Sprouts have been chopped back as much as once a year for seven consecutive years and survived to become healthy trees. Forest Service studies show that light burning and heaping of soil against stumps actually stimulates sprouting frequency in some cases.

The persistence of sprouts helps account for the late development of the north coast area. Settlers who tried to clear the land for grazing and agriculture met frustration in their attempts to create what are called "stump ranches" in forested regions elsewhere. Weedlike, the redwood is almost impossible to eradicate. Stumps, with their wide-ranging, sprouting roots, could only be removed by blasting. Grass, sowed between stumps for pasturing, was smothered out by new trees within a few years.

Most of the homesteaders gave up. One large "ranch" in Mendocino County has been logged twice, burned repeatedly, and grazed by both sheep and cattle for a hundred years. Today, it's well stocked with a healthy crop of stump-grown trees that will soon be ready for the third harvest.

An industry publicity man has compared this characteristic with the indestructible, fast-multiplying schmoo of comic-strip fame. For even with its trunk removed and as much as forty percent of its old root system chopped away, the tree survives and continues to sprout.

Using the still-living root system of its parent stump, the shoot gains a head start in life. This instant supply of moisture and nourishment allows it to quickly rise above competing vegetation and out of range of tree-nibbling deer and rabbits. The widespread old roots, revitalized, continue to serve as a moisture trap and, to a degree unmatched by other commercial species, help keep the soil in place.

The redwood's habit of adventitious crown sprouting qualifies it for what scientists know as a genotype, a tree reproduced from an original plant. Most of the sempervirens standing today—some say as many as ninety percent—have grown from stump sprouts, not seeds. It is tempting to imagine that a young tree could be growing from a root system that is thousands or millions of years old, though no forester has yet documented such an opinion. The probability that many trees have grown, fallen, and been succeeded on the same spot makes the term "second growth," commonly applied to young trees elsewhere, meaningless in the redwoods.

Forest visitors often come across evidence of stump sprouting in the close circle of large trees called a "fairy ring," where as many as a dozen youngsters have sprouted from all sides of the same parent stump and root system. As time passes, the weaker members of the family circle will be crowded out and die, unless removed by a thinning harvest.

No other commercial conifer reproduces from sprouts and none is able to sprout at any season of the year. Even the Sierra redwood lacks this ability and, due to ecological upsets, may be threatened as a species because it must rely on reproduction by seed alone.

The redwood's coppice growth process is almost tamper-proof by man, beast, or disaster. Such reserve force and rejuvenating power, Jepson noted, is probably not surpassed by any other tree. Over a period of time, it is obvious to the forest observer that this is the primary means the redwood has used to maintain itself and prolong its geologic life.

Encouraging this more dependable natural means of regeneration, instead of relying entirely on seeds and seedlings, became the foundation for today's intensive forest-management practices in the redwoods.

The plodding, the empiricism, and the mistakes of the early fern hoppers were essential in forming a body of knowledge about the idiosyncrasies of redwood regrowth. Here are some of the things they and their successors have found:

Stump shoots will grow up beneath the shade of older trees, but seedlings usually do not.

Sprouts have a universally high survival rate. It's different with seedlings, particularly in the drier southern half of the region, where five or six months without rain can take a heavy toll of fledgling trees.

Seeds dropped from trees average only about twenty percent viability, though as Fritz discovered, their vast numbers often make up for the lost potential.

But to germinate and survive to year-old seedling stage, the seeds need soil that has been disturbed in some manner—by flood, fire, or logging activity. For the redwoods dump as much as ten tons of needles to the acre annually, creating a thick carpet on the ground that can dry out the young trees in the summer sun, "damp them off" in winter moisture, or kill them by a widely prevalent fungus disease.

There is a further theory that the tree is even incapable of producing seed cones in some areas unless the root system has been impaired by ground disturbance. Another holds that the reason for the low viability of the redwood's seeds is that over the centuries it has come to depend on sprouting, rather than seeding, as the principal means of perpetuating itself.

Yet the redwood seed is far from being obsolete. Postlogging reseeding by helicopter has proved an effective method of supplementing stump sprouting to regenerate a thicker forest faster.

Cone-collecting for seeds has become a minor falltime industry in the region. But today's nursery men are hard to please. Because seeds pass on the growth characteristics of their parents, only those cones from trees of good form, at selected locations and elevations, are acceptable for the drying and seed-separating process.

Despite the failure of the Redwood Reforestation Association experiment of four decades ago, the hand-planting of seedlings is still done on some industrial forests. However, as State Service Forester Phillip Lowell points out, it is an expensive, complex, last-resort measure to get the forest growing again.

To better the odds for survival in the sunnier southern part of the range, foresters are experimenting with artificial shade in the form of shingles stuck in the ground on the sunny side of the seedlings. Applications are made to the soil to improve its moisture-holding ability and to make seedling roots extend downward more rapidly. Various chemicals and oils are being sprayed on young trees to find a medium that will prevent drying out.

No matter what has happened to the land where redwood once grew, there's a good chance that the forest will regenerate itself sooner or later without man's help. But sooner or later is a phrase that finds no favor among foresters.

On difficult sites, where cutover land does not naturally reforest itself quickly or is otherwise not completely stocked with new trees, many redwood forest landowners have undertaken a continuous land-rehabilitation program. Like other farmers, they use tractors to remove weeds and disk the soil in preparation for the next crop. This exposes the needed mineral soil bed and removes competing plants. The problem areas are then reseeded from the air or replanted by logging crews in the off season with young trees from industrial nurseries. Several thousand acres a year get this special treatment.

In their efforts to make the land more productive, redwood foresters have a natural advantage in the growth rate of their tree, which to outsiders seems incredible.

Who's going to believe—even in the Californian land of superlatives—that you can grow a merchantable tree a hundred feet tall in a little more than twenty years? Or that within a century it is possible to regrow a forest of trees taller than the tallest in Muir Woods National Monument?

It has been done. But these unusual examples demonstrate again that the Redwood Region is not one, but two separate forests. To duplicate a Muir Woods, a Big Basin, or a Stout Grove requires the best combination of soil, moisture, and growing conditions.

A hint of the wide variations of site quality is given in the tables worked out by the UC School of Forestry, used to estimate the expected growth and yield of future harvests. The eight site indexes applied to coast redwood forest land are given numbers to match the average height of the regrowth trees at one hundred years of age. To the amazement of foresters elsewhere in the world, the highest redwood site class is rated 240 feet. The second best site grows 220-foot-tall trees in a century, while others range down to 100 feet.

Horizontally, redwood trunks add about half an inch in diameter each year to the age of forty, when they slow down, reaching an average thickness of twenty-eight inches at one hundred years.

To determine just how fast a redwood can grow, scientists at California Institute of Technology recently established ideal indoor conditions, with controlled temperature, and almost literally watched the trees add height. Some of the seedlings were climbing at the dizzying rate of more than 4½ inches a day, or nearly a quarter of an inch each hour.

But height is of minor importance to those who grow crops for conversion to products. What matters is the volume of fibers suitable for lumber, plywood, pulp, and hardboard. And here coast redwood clinches its title to the fastest growing of America's cone-bearing trees, unequaled in its capacity to produce wood volume. In its prime age on the best sites, an acre of trees is capable of growing as much as six thousand board feet a year, or about enough to pave three tennis courts with boards an inch thick. Throughout the region, the average

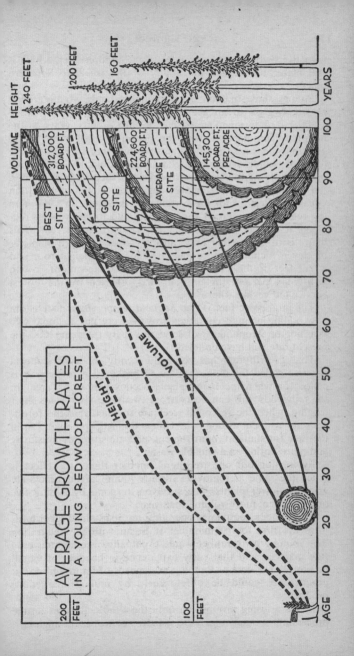

annual growth is a more modest eight hundred feet, which is still better than twice the ability of the weedlike Southern pines.

Studies show that on average-quality lands, young-growth redwoods grow at an average annual rate of from 1,100 to 1,500 board feet per acre from the age of fifty years to the hundred-year mark. This is the period of their most useful growth. Since these rates usually prevail from age zero to the fifty- or hundred-year age class, they could be maintained permanently at that level with repeated successive croppings.

Put all the growth figures together, as consultant John Gleason Miles did for the National Park Service in 1963, and the region's commercial forests are found to be growing redwood at the net rate of 620 million board feet a year. This figure is for sawtimber only, meaning trees having a diameter of eleven inches or more measured at breast height four and a half feet up the trunk. Not unexpectedly the rate of growth is fifty-six percent higher than that reported by the Forest Service ten years earlier.

The impressive fact is that *Sequoia sempervirens* forests are now adding enough cubic net growth every day to build two Washington Monuments of solid wood. By the year 2000 the present rate will have doubled.

That growth rate has zoomed recently by a silvicultural practice called thinning, familiar to backyard gardeners. It is called for when too many plants occupy a growing area. In the redwoods, this can occur from twenty to sixty years after logging, when the regrowth trees are so thick that the foresters refer to them as dog hair. Unless thinned, some will fail in the race for sunlight, nourishment, and moisture, dying slowly and representing an avoidable waste.

By logging out one tree here, another there, the effect is much the same as removing surplus young carrots or closely growing flower plants. The survivors respond by adding five or ten percent more volume each year.

The lumber companies operating on a sustained-yield basis were the first to try thinning. It began with the realization that young-growth timber would eventually become their only raw material and that early experience in handling it would be useful. The cost of thinning as a means of improving forest productivity could be offset partly by milling marketable products.

It was a losing proposition until the 1960's. Returns on the processing of small logs were usually not worth the high cost of logging between standing trees. Whatever market existed for the young stuff was for many years limited to small poles, two-by-fours, and low-grade uses.

The first encouragement came with development of the lightweight, rubber-tired tractors the loggers call kittens—too small to be cats—which for the first time made it possible to selectively log economically among small trees.

Then came a housing boom in Japan, where the building rate of 1.9 million dwelling units a year now surpasses the U.S. rate by nearly twenty percent. The federal government has been encouraging the export of lumber and logs from the Pacific Coast as a means of balancing international trade, with a resulting strong market for "toothpick" logs too small to be used in domestic mills. Huge, specially built ships are loading the redwood thinnings at Port Orford, Eureka, San Francisco, and Redwood City. At a reasonable level, the continuing sale of these surplus logs represents a means of boosting both the region's economy and the overall growth rate of the forest.

The advantages of thinning are shown on a Georgia-Pacific Corporation test plot of forty-six-year-old trees north of Eureka. Containing an average of fifty-five thousand board feet per acre, it was thinned by removing one third of the trees. Within five years, growth spurted and the remaining redwoods added back sixty percent of the volume removed. Growth rate increased twenty-one percent a year. At the end of ten years, the stand contained more board-foot volume than when it was first cut.

Another influence on the improvement of private forests has been the national Tree Farm program of American Forest Institute. From an idea planted in Washington State in 1941, it has since grown to cover seventy million acres of forest land.

In the redwoods, the Joy Woods Tree Farm in Sonoma County in 1947 became the first to sign up. Three years later, California Redwood Association took on the local certifying task and a formal program began with 108,000 acres in four counties.

Tree farmers voluntarily agree to keep their land continuously productive; to protect it from fire, insects, and disease and animal damage. Suitable multiple use of the forests is encouraged. Contrary to common belief, there is no tax advantage of any kind in tree farming.

To tack up the diamond Tree Farm sign, an owner of ten or more acres of forest first applies to either AFI, the sponsoring CRA, or the Redwood Region Conservation Council. A forester inspects the acreage and, if it qualifies, passes it on to the RRCC's Tree Farm committee. Following committee approval, a certificate and sign are issued by CRA.

Tree farms are reinspected from time to time, and those few not meeting the standards are dropped. Others may have been converted to residential or recreational uses. A half-dozen certificates have been withdrawn in as many years and the number of tree farms in the region remains fairly constant at about 125.

In size, the program grows steadily. There are now 800,000 acres enrolled and sponsors have reason to hope that the total will top a million by the early 1970's.

Tree farmers are entitled to professional advice on how to manage their lands and receive mailings that the sponsoring agencies believe might be helpful. RRCC conducts occasional seminars for tree farmers, featuring speakers on the thinning of young-growth forests, market conditions, public recreation, and watershed protection.

The practice of forest conservation has come a long way since the University's circuit riders first took the forestry gospel into the redwoods. It has taken a battalion of professional foresters and a half century of hit-and-miss experience to bring our knowledge to its present state, which, in comparison with that known about other species of trees, is still a seedling.

In 1930, there were less than a dozen graduate foresters working for redwood companies. Today, the seven member firms of California Redwood Association alone can count a total of sixty-one employed full-time in the redwoods.

All operating companies employ staff professionals who give guidance on land management and conduct continuing studies. Some smaller firms hire part-time consultants.

The men who tend the nation's most productive forest land work with educational institutions, private research groups, and public agencies such as the U.S. Bureau of Sport Fisheries and Wildlife, county agricultural departments, and the state departments of fish and game, conservation, and agriculture.

Staffs of foresters and specialized scientists are at work on a wide range of studies at the UC School of Forestry and Conservation, the Wildland Research Center, the California Agricultural Experiment Station, the Agricultural Extension Service, and the Forest Service's Pacific Southwest Forest and

Range Experiment Station, all headquartered within sight of the redwoods at Berkeley.

Some are modern woodsmen in white who seldom leave their laboratories. There are geologists, ecologists, plant physiologists, and specialists of several disciplines who work with the "dirt foresters" in the field to learn how man and nature can live in harmony.

Following up the regional foresters' reputation as being the first in the nation to employ aerial photos in forest-type mapping and timber cruising, today's redwood experts make use of such Space Age helps as neutron probes, computers, infrared photography, radio-isotopes, and even space-orbiting satellites.

Contributing pieces to the redwoods' scientific jigsaw puzzle, the U.S. Forest Service at its 995-acre Yurok Experimental Forest near the Klamath River has been testing three basic harvesting methods in converting old stands into younger, managed forests. In addition to clear-cut blocks and selective logging, researchers are trying shelterwood cutting, in which large seed trees are left after removal of seventy-five percent of the stand's volume.

Students at Humboldt State College, one of the nation's largest forestry schools, often use redwood logging operations near Arcata as outdoor classrooms and work on their own experimental forest provided by a lumber company.

The State Division of Forestry, in formal cooperation with the Forest Service and lumber companies, continues field experiments and research in forest genetics, fire control, reforestation, plant physiology, rodent control, and stream protection at its test-tube redwood forest near Fort Bragg. Other forestry experts work out of division offices in Monterey, Willits, and Santa Rosa.

Extension foresters are employed by Humboldt and Mendocino counties.

Collectively, the private and governmental experts have a tough assignment: to help achieve something called sustained yield. That's the magic balance between the amount of timber cut and the amount grown, which will assure perpetual forests and perpetual forest benefits.

The job is complicated by the fact that a large amount of redwood forest acreage consists of virgin or old-growth trees growing at an average annual rate of only 130 board feet—one tenth that of vigorous young growth. The oldest trees are likely to be losing wood volume due to progressive deterioration of the heartwood.

In California state parks, for example, the average timber volume of the redwoods is ninety-five thousand board feet per acre. Yet this volume can be grown in seventy years on average commercial forest sites, forty-five years on good sites, and in only thirty-one years on the best sites.

The commercial redwood forest now provides eighteen percent of California's sawtimber from all sources cut each year, but produces only fourteen percent of the average annual net growth. The gap will soon be closed with the aid of what some foresters call the primary tool of forestry, the chain saw. Declining trees will be replaced with growing trees on a continuous basis and the waste of the land's productive potential will be ended.

Some redwood companies and the state's Jackson Forest have now reached the sustained-yield level. Other companies are managing their forests for eventual sustained yield, but, due to varying amounts of old and overmature trees, will not reach a balance for years—in some cases, not in this century.

The Miles study showed that for the Redwood Region as a whole, the total cubic-foot growth on commercial forest land will be in balance with the cut in 1975. On sawtimber larger than eleven inches in diameter, the average annual net growth is expected to equal the harvest in 1985. Barring large reallocations of multipurpose land to single use, the redwood forest can produce a level of wood volume equal to the mid-1960's cut each year into the future.

The outlook is brightened by practices—planned and accidental—that tend to increase the number of redwoods and extend its range. More trees are being grown now because of the redwood's habit of stump-sprouting and its bully-like dominance of other vegetation.

Most of the commercial redwood forest consists of mixed stands. After logging, the redwood stumps soon sprout new trees, while the fir, spruce, hemlock and other conifers will not. Without further manipulation by man, the ratio of regrowth redwoods in the new forest will be higher than in the old. If the area has been selectively cut, the seeds of other species will have a difficult time getting established under the partial shade of the trees left behind, and may be squeezed out eventually by the faster-growing redwoods. A 1966 study by the State Board of Forestry revealed that an original stand containing forty percent redwood trees and sixty percent whitewoods within six years after logging was growing eighteen percent more redwoods than before. Eight times as many redwoods came back naturally after the Henry Creek area of Humboldt and Mendocino counties was logged, according to the California Forest and Range Experiment Station.

In the case of clear-cutting, the forester may juggle the ratio of seeds in the follow-up planting by air and has the option of duplicating the original species mix or increasing the proportion of redwoods in the new forest.

"To play it safe," explains Chief Forester Brown of Miller Redwood Co., whose operations are typical, "we aim to establish at least ten trees for each one we harvest."

Because it will eventually overtop any other tree species in the region, all the redwood needs is a start. The Pacific Northwest Forest and Range Experiment Station cites the example that ninety percent of the land now bearing hardwood trees in Humboldt County is capable of growing redwoods. Some lumber companies are now logging and utilizing the formerly worthless alders, maples and chinquapins, and re-seeding the land with redwoods.

Afforestation projects are carried out by youth groups, schools, and Boy Scouts throughout the region with the help of an average of twenty-five thousand seedlings a year donated by the California Redwood Association and the Redwood Region Conservation Council. The State Highway Department plants sempervirens wherever possible as roadside decoration. In Sacramento, the old city dump has been planted and, who knows, may someday qualify as another redwood park.

But not everyone, it seems, is trying to grow more redwoods faster. Researchers at California Institute of Technology, in their quest for combinations of chemicals that affect plant growth, have succeeded in completely, stopping the growth of sempervirens. An Eastern nursery man has advertised the ultimate affront to the tallest of trees. For twenty-five dollars you may decorate your dining-room table with a living midget redwood in a bonzai planter.

The miniaturization of the redwood underscores its great adaptability. There's no question that nature's selective-breeding process has been responsible for the tree's tenacity through the ages. Competition within local strains has eliminated weaker trees, leaving those best able to carry on.

Seeds from carefully selected "plus trees" are being grown at forest nurseries which will eventually yield supertrees that are taller, straighter, healthier, and contain more knot-free wood than the average.

The game that tree-breeders play, explains Dr. William J. Libby of UC, is to pass on only those characteristics of the tree most useful to man to the next generation of trees.

In this combination of natural and artificial selection processes, why not then experiment with the most promising tree of them all?

Soon after the world's tallest tree was discovered a few years ago, a hunting party visited the Redwood Creek site and, with the aid of a scope-sighted .22-caliber rifle, fired bullets 350 feet into its upper foliage. The men were forest scientists, and admittedly not very good marksmen, whose hunting was for samples of the branches to be used in rooting and grafting.

Their reason for collecting shoots and cuttings instead of seeds reveals another unique characteristic of this strange plant. Chromosomes, carrying the hereditary genes that determine a tree's future, are twenty to twenty-six in number in all cone-bearing species. But not in sempervirens, which has an inexplicable sixty-six. This complicates the tree's reproductive process and may allow greater variation between individuals. This, in turn, offers forest geneticists a rare opportunity. Since coast redwood theoretically has three times as many chances to be different, and because shoots and cuttings, unlike seeds, pass on all the parent's chromosomes, they may be selected and cultivated to regenerate any of the tree's many variations.

In a redwood genetics project underwritten by Arcata Redwood Co. and the National Science Foundation, Professor Libby is studying the special characteristics of the tallest tree's scions. He deals with the intriguing possibility that these offspring may be used to artificially generate a forest of supertrees, of a height and growth rate never known to man.

Soon—as time would be measured by the redwood—might not our scientific knowledge be applied to regrowing the tree where it once flourished around the planet ten, twenty, or fifty million years ago?

Few other useful trees have such potential. And in the overpopulated years ahead, it may be possible with the aid of chemicals and desalinated seawater to grow community forests and woodlots of specially developed strains of the remarkable redwood to provide fiber crops for many peoples, serving their product and aesthetic needs just as it has in California since the time of the padres.

## Chapter X

# They Saved the Redwoods

"A national park is our last-chance opportunity to save the redwoods," said the President of the United States in a 1967 appeal to Congress.

It is a warning that has been heard by every generation of citizens for a hundred years. Almost as long as there has been a State of California, there have been proposals for a federal park in the redwoods.

About a dozen of them were serious attempts to create a large park in seven different locations. The goals of nearly all of the proposals have been achieved—but not by the federal government.

Another president, that of the Save-the-Redwoods League, admits to being confused by the widespread use of the terms "last chance" and "the last of the redwoods." "There aren't any last redwoods," Dr. Ralph W. Chaney told a group of Girl Scouts touring the North Coast. "The redwoods are saved."

Over the years, the mystic beauty of the tree itself may have been its best protection. Anyone who has seen a grove of old redwoods, even through an automobile window, becomes an advocate for preservation. The sight stirs some deep, silent litany passed on unremembered from our tree-worshipping ancestors. There is little wonder that the mystique has inspired a seventy-year program of preservation marking a high point in the history of man's concern for his surroundings.

It started in Gold Rush days. Henry A. Crabb introduced a resolution in the 1852 session of the California Assembly asking the federal government to prohibit, "the settlement and occupation of all public lands upon which Red Wood is growing." Though the lower house passed Crabb's resolution, it was doomed to oblivion because of his surprising lack of knowledge of the subject. It might be suspected that Crabb had never ventured into the thick forests of his adopted state —in recent years second only to Oregon as a log producer— when he wrote as preamble, "WHEREAS the lands of California are sparsely wooded and timber for building purposes is extremely scarce and difficult to be procured. . . ."

Others seeking to preserve coast redwoods would pick up the scarcity theme over the years and help manufacture a mythology as persistent as redwood sprouts.

"In 10 years," warned Charles Graham in an 1886 *Harper's Weekly* article, "Sequoia sempervirens will exist in California only as curiosities." Ten years later, Carrie Stevens Walker told her *Overland Monthly* readers that "but a decade is needed for their complete extinction." The species will be extinct "at no remote period," said a *National Geographic* writer in 1899. There remains but "a few years supply at most," and coast redwood will "soon be scarce" and "gone forever," wrote three other prophets of the last century.

The writers and editors of fifty or one hundred years ago might be excused on the basis that their cry-wolf technique was justified in order to stir an apathetic public to action. The motives of some government officials are more obscure. The first of the doom-predicting politicians to go on record was the president of the California Board of Agriculture in 1868. He reported that there was only a forty-year supply of timber left and that "Europe will, in a very few years, own greater forests of our valuable redwood trees than California ever could boast of."

The State Board of Forestry in 1889 warned, "In less than forty years our redwood forests will exist but in theory."

The years 1908 and 1929 came and went, as did all the other deadlines for disaster, but the faulty prophesies continue to this day. "The Last Redwoods," "The Wasted Woods," and "Zero Hour in the Redwoods," admonishes the Sierra Club. Humboldt County will be completely devoid of old-growth trees by 1968, said a state college professor in 1965.

Collectively, the doom-sayers helped in their sometimes

questionable way to establish the present system of over seventy coast redwood parks and reservations. And they may have been an influence also in hastening the day when sustained-yield forestry came to private lands. Earlier, when little was known about the regrowth powers of the redwood and even less about its management, there was reasonable cause for concern.

At least one third of every tree cut was being wasted in 1879, when Secretary of the Interior Carl Schurz recommended that Congress set aside forty-six thousand acres of the public domain. It was the first serious proposal for a federal park in the coast redwoods.

Congress then began its long history of ignoring such proposals and the establishment of the first redwood park was left to the State of California and some of its concerned citizens.

One of them was a Redwood City newspaper editor who in the 1880's echoed Schurz' appeal and advocated a large national park in southern San Mateo and northern Santa Cruz counties. The campaign lost some of its momentum when it was revealed that the editor's enthusiasm may have been influenced by his interest in the Spring Valley Water Co., which was known to want a permanent cover for its Pescadero watershed.

Phoebe Hearst, mother of the well-known publisher, soon after put up the funds for a campaign to preserve the outstanding trees in the Big Basin area, about twenty miles north of Santa Cruz. The State Board of Forestry lent official support. In 1899, San Jose photographer Andrew P. Hill joined the crusade and was instrumental in calling a public meeting at Stanford University, where a committee of eight citizens was formed to investigate the Big Basin proposal on the ground.

Around their campfire in the woods the night of May 18, 1900, the inspecting committee formed the Sempervirens Club and vowed to push the project through.

The legislature was persuaded the next year to authorize the purchase of 2,500 acres of old-growth redwoods for one hundred dollars an acre. It was the beginning of California's state park system. It was the beginning also of a tradition of cooperation between the redwood industry and preservation interests that has never ended: Lumberman Henry L. Middleton donated an additional 1,300 acres of land to the new Big

Basin Redwoods State Park. The greatest preservation program for a single species of tree had begun with a total of 3,800 acres.

National Park proposals continued. Congressman Raker of California in 1911 introduced a joint resolution calling for a committee to investigate the "advisability and necessity" of such a park, but it joined the Crabb and Schurz proposals in limbo.

Private efforts to save the best of the redwoods for the future were more successful. Joseph W. Welch in 1867 acquired 350 acres of the old Sansevain land grant in Santa Cruz County and operated it as a semipublic park. It is now part of Henry W. Cowell Redwoods State Park.

Col. James B. Armstrong was a lumberman in the Russian River area who believed that a part of his landholdings should be available to the public. In the 1890's, he tried to donate his 440-acre tract to the state, but under the laws of the time the government could not accept it. The colonel preserved the area nevertheless, and in 1917 it was acquired by Sonoma County and eventually became Armstrong Redwoods State Park.

In 1903, a private group headed by William Randolph Hearst acquired historic Fort Ross and three years later handed it over to the state.

William Kent came from Illinois and fell under the spell of the Marin County redwoods. In 1905, he and his wife bought six hundred acres of land, including Redwood Canyon at the foot of Mt. Tamalpais. The price was seventy-five dollars an acre. When the North Coast Water Co. a year later threatened to condemn the canyon for a dam, Kent wrote to his friend, President Theodore Roosevelt, offering to donate half the property to the government under the newly passed Antiquities Act.

"Bully," responded the Rough Rider, and we shall call it Kent Woods.

Kent refused. "To stencil one's name on a benefaction seems to carry with it an implication of mundane immortality as being something purchasable."

"By George! You are right," replied the President. "It is enough to do the deed."

Kent suggested that the park be named in honor of John Muir, who had done so much to preserve the redwoods of the

Sierra. In 1908, it was accepted by the government as the nucleus of Muir Woods National Monument.

More people were exposed to the attractions of redwood country when steel rails linked San Francisco Bay with Eureka in 1914, and an alternately muddy or dusty Redwood Highway straggled behind. The traveling salesmen, vacationers, and sightseers who now penetrated the deep redwoods took home an unforgettable memory and a hope that the best of the great northern groves would be saved.

Only about five thousand acres of coast redwoods were in any type of reserve three years later, when a distinguished group of campers made their way up the new highway route. They were Madison Grant, chairman of the New York Zoological Society; Dr. John C. Merriam of UC, later president of the Carnegie Institution; and Dr. Fairfield Osborn, president of the American Museum of Natural History. Alarmed at the advance of logging toward the best groves, and by the work of highway builders who were routing their rights-of-way through the lowland redwoods, they decided the time had come for action outside of government channels.

With the help of some equally distinguished friends, including the chiefs of the National Park Service and the Forest Service, they formed the Save-the-Redwoods League in 1918. Franklin K. Lane, a former Secretary of the Interior, was elected president. Publicity would be vital to the enterprise, so the directors hired the Drury Advertising Co. of San Francisco and appointed Newton B. Drury secretary.

Fund-raising was soon added to the league's objectives, and with one hundred dollars in the treasury, one of conservation's greatest success stories was begun. In its first year of operation, four thousand members were signed up and brought with them $140,000.

In 1920, the league coaxed Congressman Clarence F. Lea to introduce a resolution asking the Secretary of the Interior to look into "the suitability, location, and cost if any, and advisability of securing a National Redwood Park." The result was the Redington Report, which recommended a 64,000-acre unit on the lower Klamath River, a half-mile-wide parkway along parts of the Redwood Highway, and 1,800 acres on the South Fork of the Eel. Preservationists rallied under the slogan of "A Redwood National Park—Now or Never!" The House passed an enabling act, but the proposal died in Senate committee.

Since government was not doing the necessary job of protecting outstanding examples of the coast redwoods, then the league must. Drury and his officers became persuasive salesmen, taking their appeals to influential citizens, politicians, service organizations, and timberland owners.

In 1921, their efforts paid off in the acquisition of two thousand acres of the future Humboldt Redwoods State Park, near the forks of the Eel River. State funds of $300,000 and donations of four lumber companies helped. Forty miles south, lumbermen Edward R. Hickey and Miles Standish made a gift of much of the timberland for the state park that now bears their name. In 1922, a five-hundred-acre grove near Garberville was converted from a private resort to a state park named in honor of Governor Friend W. Richardson.

Two years later, a grove of trees named for pioneer lumberman Joseph Russ and his wife was donated as the beginning of Prairie Creek State Park.

The league was the guiding spirit in the creation of a State Park Commission and Division of Beaches and Parks in 1927 and the passage of a six-million-dollar park bond act in 1928.

But the crusaders' greatest achievement in the 1920's was the wresting from the legislature of an agreement unique in the history of park acquisition anywhere. It calls for the state to match funds donated to the league, dollar for dollar, to be used in buying redwoods. With only a few exceptions, the arrangement eventually produced the outstanding system of thirty parks which the state classifies as coast-redwood type.

Several friendly devices were employed to attract contributions and bequests. An early one was "the $10,000 tour," in which prospects were taken on a topless touring-car trip under the trees. One such drive routed the late John D. Rockefeller, Jr., through what the league called "the most majestic forest since the beginning of time." It resulted in a two-million-dollar contribution that helped purchase the breathtaking stand of three-hundred-foot-tall trees growing on the flats along Bull Creek. Rockefeller Forest is now a part of the 43,000-acre Humboldt Redwoods State Park.

Another successful donation-raiser has been the league's memorial-grove program. More than two hundred groves in redwood state parks have been named for benefactors or members of their families.

Drury, his brother Aubrey, and top officials of the league

were successful in convincing lumbermen that some of their best timberlands had a higher public value than for lumber. They sought a permanent moratorium on cutting in selected areas until the state or the league could find the money to buy it.

Nearly every company they approached agreed to cooperate, though it usually meant some kind of financial loss. The Pacific Lumber Co. held one choice 2,100-acre unit for forty years. In a recent year this cost $33,000 in timber and land taxes. Simpson Timber Co. held an eight-hundred-acre parcel adjoining Jedediah Smith State Park for ten years at a tax cost of $142,000. Fire-protection, insurance and patrol are other costs while the gentleman's agreements are in effect. Several thousand acres of outstanding groves in three counties are still held in trust. Many of the attractions of the redwood state parks would not be available today if such agreements, bound only by a handshake, had not been secured.

Further proof of the league's effectiveness is found in the fact that in only a few instances have lumber companies resorted to the courts to fix a fair price for the future parkland.

From the beginning, each purchase was priority-chosen. The state and the league sought to secure the best groves first. Because this often meant the large trees growing in pure stands on streamside flats and benches, it was, acre for acre, the most costly of any forested parkland to acquire.

The league took its appeal for funds to people everywhere. Donations came from the concerned and the sentimental, rich and poor. Schoolchildren's pennies mixed with the fortunes of labor unions, philanthropists, foundations, and corporations. The Soroptimists, Izaak Walton League, Boy Scouts, Garden Clubs of America, and even Hoo-Hoo, the lumbermen's association, serve as a sample of the wide range of organizations that have contributed. Many of the gifts were large enough to be honored with the naming of a grove. Quite a few have been made anonymously.

Dollar by dollar, acre by acre, the park system grew. A half-dozen donation-dependent conservation organizations, and even government officials, in their crusades raise the old cry that the redwoods must be saved from the loggers' saws. The less sensational truth is that the best of the redwoods have more often been saved for the public by the lumbermen themselves.

Being in a position to serve the cause of preservation, they have responded with a generosity probably unequaled by any other industrial group. Among the donors of redwood land to the state or the league appear the names of Albion Lumber Co., Boulder Creek Land & Timber Co., Georgia-Pacific Corp., Grizzly Lumber Co., Hammond Lumber Co., The Pacific Lumber Co., Sage Land & Lumber Co., and Simpson Timber Co. Timbermen Cheatham, Lancaster, Pamplin, Reed, Russ, Tyson, and Vance are among those memorialized by named groves. Scenic Fern Canyon in Prairie Creek State Park and a portion of the Avenue of the Giants were gifts of The Pacific Lumber Co. Famed Stout Grove was donated by a lumber company in the 1930's to become the nucleus of Jedediah Smith State Park.

Though of little moment amid the near-immortality of the redwoods, it will be news to users of some of the state reserves to learn that entire parks have been named to honor the foresight and generosity of their principal donors: Taylor, Montgomery, Armstrong, Standish, Hickey, Van Damme, Dimmick, and Hendy—redwood lumbermen all.

The Georgia-Pacific Corp. in 1969 quietly turned over its spectacular Van Duzen River groves for addition to Grizzly Creek Redwoods State Park. It was a six million dollar gesture, hailed by the Nature Conservancy as "the largest single gift ever made by an American firm for conservation purposes."

This "widest cooperation evidenced by the men of business concerned with lumber operations," as a president of the league once described it, was formalized by the California Redwood Association more than forty years ago. The leading redwood manufacturers adopted a resolution supporting the upcoming state park bond issue, urging that "a large and representative area of virgin redwood timber be secured and set aside, for all time," as a state park, and forming a park committee of lumbermen to work in cooperation with the league and the State Park Commission.

Just after World War II, the most extravagant national park scheme of them all appeared. Congresswoman Helen Gahagan Douglas introduced a bill calling for federal purchase of 2.3 million acres of private forest land in northern California, of which 340,000 acres would be a park. As had all other federal overtures, this redwood park fizzled and its sponsor was replaced by Richard Nixon at the next election.

An interesting sidelight is provided by Newton Drury, then serving as director of the National Park Service. "There are those who ask why it would not be desirable to move toward the establishment of a redwood national park," he wrote in 1946, "My candid answer to that would be that I should favor this if it were feasible, but I do not think it is. Surely the coast redwoods merit this designation—they are among the wonders of the world—but the fact is that the best and most representative of these forests are now in the California state parks. They are being carefully and intelligently protected."

While the league has become synonymous with redwood park acquisition, it has not been alone. The State Parks Agency—also once headed by Drury—from its birth in 1927 has been successful in convincing the legislature that time was shorter than tax money. Using proceeds from the general fund, offshore-oil revenues, and bond money, an aggressive redwood-acquisition program continues. In this manner, all California citizens have helped.

Some land gifts have not gone through the league, and in a few cases, state land was traded with private owners on an equal-value basis to save the best redwoods. On other occasions, land went to the state after some of the timber was cut.

The Nature Conservancy was instrumental in bringing the Georgia-Pacific groves and the future Andrew Solera park into the state system. They accepted the Forest of Nisene Marks on behalf of the state after the Marks family had refused a land developer's offer of four million dollars for the property.

Conservation Associates deserves most of the credit for presenting Castle Rock Park to the public and enlarging Big Basin State Park.

Several county governments have contributed land to state parks, while seven others maintain their own redwood reserves.

In 1966 federal money for the first time became available for the coast redwoods. Through the Land and Water Conservation Fund program, two million dollars were allocated to buy a section of the Avenue of the Giants, extending it to nine miles in length.

Dedication of this unit in 1968 marked the golden anniversary of the league. In its fifty years, the citizen group, now forty-three thousand strong, has helped create the atmosphere of concern and cooperation responsible for saving the best of the coast redwoods—280 square miles of them. Its living monument is a green garland of seventy parks and reserves, beginning with Loeb State Park in Oregon, through the Red-

## COAST REDWOOD STATE PARKS

| NAME | COUNTY | ACRES | camp sites | picnic | swim | fish | ocean beach | trailers |
|------|--------|------:|-----------:|:------:|:----:|:----:|:-----------:|:--------:|
| Julia Pfeiffer Burns | Monterey | 1,700 | | X | | | | |
| Pfeiffer-Big Sur | Monterey | 822 | 218 | X | X | X | | X |
| Andrew Molera (future) | Monterey | 2,100 | | | | | | |
| Forest Nisene Marks | Santa Cruz | 9,779 | | | | | | |
| Henry Cowell | Santa Cruz | 1,737 | 51 | X | X | X | | |
| Big Basin | Santa Cruz | 11,886 | 332 | X | | X | | X |
| Castle Rock | Santa Cruz | 513 | | | | | | |
| Butano | San Mateo | 2,186 | 40 | | | | | |
| Portola | San Mateo | 1,740 | 60 | X | X | X | | |
| Mt. Tamalpais | Marin | 4,888 | 49 | X | | | | |
| Samuel P. Taylor | Marin | 2,576 | 74 | X | X | | | X |
| Armstrong | Sonoma | 560 | 45 | X | | X | | X |
| Fort Ross | Sonoma | 356 | | X | | X | X | |
| Mailliard | Mendocino | 242 | | | | X | | |
| Indian Creek | Mendocino | 15 | | X | | | | |
| Hendy Woods | Mendocino | 605 | 95 | X | X | X | | |
| Paul M. Dimmick | Mendocino | 12 | 28 | X | | X | X | |
| Montgomery Woods | Mendocino | 647 | | | | | | |
| Van Damme | Mendocino | 1,825 | 82 | X | X | X | X | |
| Adm. Wm. H. Standley | Mendocino | 45 | | X | X | X | | |
| Standish-Hickey | Mendocino | 915 | 159 | X | X | X | | |
| Smithe | Mendocino | 462 | | | X | X | | |
| Reynolds Flat | Mendocino | 375 | 50 | X | X | X | | |
| Richardson Grove | Humboldt | 831 | 185 | X | X | X | | |
| Benbow Lake | Humboldt | 498 | | X | X | X | | |
| Humboldt | Humboldt | 43,718 | 245 | X | X | X | | X |
| Grizzly Creek | Humboldt | 234 | 30 | X | X | X | | |
| Prairie Creek* | Humboldt | 12,241 | 150 | X | | X | X | X |
| Del Norte Coast* | Del Norte | 6,375 | 142 | X | | X | X | X |
| Jedediah Smith* | Del Norte | 8,852 | 107 | X | X | X | | X |
| Loeb | Curry (Ore.) | 120 | | X | | | | |
| **TOTAL** | | **118,855** | **2,142** | | | | | |

* Managed cooperatively with Redwood National Park.

wood National Park and two dozen state parks, stretching more than five hundred miles south to below the Big Sur. Aside from land donations, the league has raised about fifteen million dollars, nearly half the price paid by the State of California for the system of redwood parks it purchased. Its monetary value today is close to half a billion dollars, its intangibles priceless.

Every type of coast redwood forest situation is represented in the public reserves owned by federal, state, county and municipal agencies, colleges, and park districts.

San Mateo County in 1968 bought 4,700 acres of old and young redwoods through the cooperation of Santa Cruz Lumber Co. Its new Pescadero Creek Park may eventually include a four-mile-long lake and expand to include three other redwood parks totaling forty thousand acres. It embraces the same area sought by Secretary Schurz in the first proposal for a national park nine decades ago.

It was a pie-in-the-sky goal back in 1919 when the Save-the-Redwoods League set out to preserve one hundred thousand acres. Drury and his benevolent "Redwood Highwaymen" have successfully used salesmanship, lobbying, cajolery, and, one suspects, occasional desk-pounding to bring into being a movement uniquely American—a private conservation effort for the benefit of the public.

Through the cooperation of government agencies, citizen groups, the private sector, and thousands of individual contributors across the country, there are now more than 180,000 acres of coast redwoods preserved for the enjoyment of all.

In reserve status is ten percent of the entire range of the species. It includes the tallest and largest sempervirens, the northernmost and southernmost groves, more than two million ancient trees, the finest forest in the world, the grove containing more board-foot volume of wood than any other on earth, the most scenic and historic examples, and, according to a Society of American Foresters report, close to a third of all the superlative old-growth groves that ever existed.

## Chapter XI

# A National Park for the Redwoods

Wall-to-wall forest makes the long valley of Redwood Creek a quiet place of natural acoustics for the human mind. No sounds of birds or animal life are heard, and fog has been a more frequent visitor than people, helping to muffle the occasional snap of a falling limb and the stream's winter roar or summer trickle. Sharp-angled hills for centuries have deposited their sediment in the valley trough to prepare a bed for giants.

Here they found the world's tallest living tree in 1963. Like a green lightning rod, it would attract the thunderbolts of history's noisiest resource controversy.

The "Mount Everest of all living things," now a feature in the southern unit of Redwood National Park, was discovered by Dr. Paul Zahl and his party during a park-scouting expedition for the National Geographic Society. Not far away, they came across the world's second, third, and fifth tallest trees.

The hiding place of the giants is an alluvial peninsula that juts into Redwood Creek eight miles upstream from its confluence with Prairie Creek at the town of Orick.

The tallest tree is two trunks grown from one, towering 367.8 feet. It weighs a million pounds. Chief Forester Eugene Hofsted of Arcata Redwood Co., on whose tree farm the find was made, estimates its age at 650 years. The grove is believed to have escaped a devastating fire about five centuries ago since most other trees in the valley are under five hundred years of age.

In redwood country, where it's hard to tell where the treetops end and the clouds begin, some of the tallest tales of all concern the tallest specimens.

In the last century, the Sierra redwood was believed to be the loftiest of plants, and the U.S. Division of Forestry pronounced the Father of the Forest to be over 400 feet tall, though 347 feet has since proved to be the record for the species. A contemporary Englishman, unconvinced, used mathematics to prove that no tree could grow higher than three hundred feet because it would come a mucker from its own weight.

A San Francisco State College geology professor in a 1965 television broadcast claimed that Eureka was once surrounded by four-hundred-foot-high coast redwoods. The Sierra Club *Bulletin* a year later announced the felling of a 390-footer near Redwood Creek. A Humboldt State College professor in 1967 told a U.S. Senate committee that he had discovered and measured a cloud-buster 385 feet tall.

The tallest coast redwood previously measured was felled about 1875 near the Russian River. It was, coincidentally, 367 feet, but an inch or so shorter than today's champion.

Taller trees had been found before. There was the Douglas fir measured by California State Forester E. T. Allen in 1900 and found to be 380 feet tall. A 385-footer was verified in 1930 as it lay on the ground near Mineral, Washington. A mountain ash in Australia measured 375 feet and there is some evidence that western cedar, Australian eucalyptus, and Canadian fir all have exceeded sempervirens in height. But taller or not, none of them are now standing.

The tallest redwood title had been held for many years by the 364-foot Founders' Tree in Humboldt Redwoods State Park forty miles south of Eureka. In 1955, lightning knocked seventeen feet off the top and the honor passed to the neighboring Dyerville Giant, 358 feet tall.

After the tall-tree discoveries on its land, Arcata Redwood Co. formed a committee of foresters and specialists to recommend means of protecting the treasures. Their earliest advice, the building of a low dike to prevent natural erosion at the site, was carried out. But the severe flood of 1964 flowed over the embankment and deposited a layer of silt across the grove. As a result, the higher ground level has reduced the measurable height of the Howard A. Libbey Tree, as the tallest had been named by the committee in honor of Arcata's president, and the new champion may be the Harry W. Cole Tree at 367.4 feet.

In 1966, a UC professor employed the National Geographic survey crew to give him a reading on another skyscraper growing near the state park's Founders' Tree. It was measured at 369 feet and proclaimed the new record-holder. But a more accurate remeasurement four months later showed it to be nine feet shorter than the Libbey Tree.

Meanwhile, the National Park Service was curious about that much-publicized 385-foot colossus reported by the Humboldt State College professor. It was located near Redwood Creek in an area just outside the boundaries of their national park proposals. With a large crew of onlookers, and the balloons, theodolites, transits, and other paraphernalia of the tree measurers, the surveyors went to work. They certified the professor's find to be 304 feet tall, about twenty percent short of the claim.

The tree may find some sort of fame, nevertheless, for a leading encyclopedia has listed it as 385 feet, and the world's tallest.

Research by UC's Dr. Paul Zinke in Australia and elsewhere indicates that sempervirens will probably hold the title of tallest species for some time. Tallest individual redwoods will come and go, as they always have. But as Zinke observes in an unprofessorlike statement, "with trees as with women, too much emphasis can be placed on measurements."

The National Geographic discovery of trees as tall as the Apollo 5 moon rocket had set the stage for a conservation confrontation that for bitterness, broad interest, contrived issues, and the establishment of precedents, itself topped them all. Like a fire deep in the damp heartwood of a Sequoia, it smolders on.

The labor pains of a national park first became evident when some concerned preservationists charged in print that Arcata Redwood Co. was planning to log the area where the new tall trees had been found. The rumor persisted, though the firm had announced in 1964 that it was dedicating the 134-acre Grove of Giants to public use.

Soon after the discovery, the National Park Service issued a report recommending three possible redwood park sites in Humboldt and Del Norte counties. Each took in the tall trees and assumed the take-over of one or more existing state parks.

A strong case for federal intervention appeared when the State Highway Department announced plans to build a freeway through nearby Prairie Creek Redwoods State Park. Its earlier work, a four-lane project that removed some large trees from Humboldt Redwoods State Park, stood as a reminder of what could happen under a state law that permitted condemnation of parklands for highways and required rights-of-way to take the most economical course.

Protests poured in to Sacramento against routings that would require the removal of old-growth trees in parks. They came from conservation groups, the State Park Commission, the governor, and the California Redwood Association.

Faced with the heavy one-way traffic in complaints, State Highway commissioners postponed plans for a Prairie Creek freeway, and the final routing is yet to be determined. But from the furor came a long-overdue victory for conservationists in the form of a changed Highway Commission policy in 1967, and a new law in 1968 which frees the Highway Department from "the shortest line between two points" requirement, placing parks on a public-interest level with roads. The highway threat to the park redwoods was over.

As enthusiasm for a national park reached the clamorous stage, state legislators became alarmed and passed a no-nonsense resolution saying that if there was going to be a federal park, it should be created entirely from existing state parks, and the state should be repaid for the loss at fair market value.

The State Park Commission issued three similar resolutions in a four-year period. Governor Edmund G. Brown and later Governor Ronald Reagan agreed, as did their appointed directors of natural resources.

Part of the official concern came from awareness that the redwood state park system had been put together largely by the donations and tax monies of California citizens.

Further, there was strong local feeling that by the mid-1960's the best of the redwoods were state-owned or pledged. State Resources Administrator Hugo Fisher pointed to "inadequate contiguous acreages of primeval redwood forest outside state parks to constitute a national park of proper scale and quality." The American Forestry Association concurred.

A new force appeared when the Sierra Club of San Francisco made the decision to do battle in the coast redwoods. The fifty-thousand-member group had its beginnings in an unsuccessful try to save picturesque Hetch-Hetch Valley from the dam-builders prior to World War I. It had lately broadened its concern for preserving wilderness in the Sierra Nevada to such issues as Colorado's Glen Canyon Dam and Washington's North Cascades National Park and saving the Colorado River above the Grand Canyon.

With the help of its two-million-dollar annual budget, the club published a rhapsodic, controversial book whose editorial approach was indicated by its title, *The Last Redwoods*.

Reacting to the strong statements of the book, some North Coast citizens and lumber-industry spokesmen came up with strong statements of their own. In this early resistance to a national park, opponents gave the impression that with a park of any size, the entire timber industry and its dependent economy would go down the drain; Muir Woods was mistakenly held up as an example of the beauty of logged-off land; park proponents were referred to in print in unprintable terms; and one local woman told a Congressional committee that the whole thing was a Communist plot.

The Sahara Club, it came to be called by some, in reference to the economic desert expected with creation of a large park.

Ill winds had appeared in 1959 and again in 1962 with storms that toppled many trees in West Coast forests. The big blowdown brought the reluctant decision of one company to clean-log down to the Redwood Highway near a state park. Among the reasons given for the action was the high loss from windthrow among seed trees left behind from earlier selective logging. The area was exposed to ocean winds across a valley meadow and several falling trees had played a game of highway Russian roulette with passing cars, including a school bus.

The resultant clear-cut logging operation was one of those "drastic, even violent upheavals often necessary in the process of creating new forests" referred to by Chief Edward P. Cliff of the U.S. Forest Service.

"We let in some daylight there alongside the road," admitted a woodsman. "But there's no doubt about it," he continued in the outspoken manner of the region, "right now she looks like Sunday morning in Hell."

"An apocalyptic devastation," concluded the Sierra Club *Bulletin*.

Though good forestry practices had been followed, and soon after reseeding and natural sprouting the area looked like a tree nursery, park proponents had found a dramatic, stump-strewn camera target. The photos were widely distributed.

In 1965 new park plans sprouted like a redwood burl. The ninety-year-old American Forestry Association announced the results of its Dana-Pomeroy study and recommended a fifty-six-thousand acre national park that would use Humboldt Redwoods State Park, eighty miles south of Redwood Creek, as a nucleus.

Conservation Associates, a San Francisco Bay Area Group, pushed its project to combine the same state park with the federal Kings Peak Range Recreation Area and create a multipurpose park of 159,000 acres.

Representative Don Clausen of the affected North Coast district presented Congress with a national park and seashore bill embracing fifty-three-thousand acres in a forty-mile strip of ocean beaches, forests, and lagoons.

An ad hoc group of Sierra Club members advocated a redwood park of 280,000 acres.

The timber industry came up with its own suggestion called the Redwood Park and Recreation Plan, which not without irony, became the first of all the proposals to approach a successful completion. Seven companies voluntarily offered a total of eight thousand acres of their redwood timberland for public park acquisition, of which two thirds has since been added to state parks. And the companion offer to open 260,000 acres of tree farm lands to free public recreation has since climbed to 350,000 acres under the continuing Redwood Industry Recreation Areas program.

The three alternate plans of the National Park Service were revised, giving Congress the choice of a park ranging from 40,000 acres to 62,000 acres in two counties, bearing price tags between $50 and $120 million.

Residents of the sparsely populated North Coast area became fearful of a poverty pocket in their backyard when they learned that the federal government for the first time in history was planning to condemn a large amount of productive land for a national park. The loss of one man's job in their timber-based economy dislocates not only the employee and his family, but also two other dependent job-holders and their families. And each acre of industrial redwood forest, estimates the U.S. Forest Service, benefits the gross national product $990 a year—every year.

Economists were hired by the administration, the industry, and the Sierra Club to determine the economic impact of various plans. The only points of agreement seemed to be that while a national park of some kind would be a desirable diversification, tourism in the area would not compensate for the economic dislocation for at least ten years. Probably much longer and possibly never, said former state and federal economist Dewayne Kreager. The offset would require about 2,500 traveling families to stay overnight in the area each night throughout the one-hundred-day tourist season.

In late 1965, California Congressman Jeffrey Cohelan of Berkeley introduced the first of many redwood national park bills that would follow in the next three years. It called for a seventy-thousand-acre park centered around the tall trees. A Senate amendment made it ninety thousand acres, with a cost of $100 million to $150 million.

Early the next year, the administration unveiled its own recommendation. The President and the Department of the Interior wanted a forty-two-thousand-acre park to be located fifty miles to the north in Mill Creek, fifteen miles from the Oregon border. It would include Jedediah Smith and Del Norte Coast state parks, as well as eighteen thousand acres of Rellim Redwood Co. land. Even this cheaper version, its detractors argued, at an estimated cost of fifty-seven million dollars for private holdings alone, would be not only the most expensive in history, but costlier than all existing national parks put together. In an attempt to aid hard-hit local government agencies, the proposal took the unprecedented step of authorizing federal payments in lieu of lost tax revenue for a five-year period.

Across the country, pressures for and against a park mounted. "Better Redwood than Deadwood" buttons appeared on UC's Berkeley campus. "Don't Park Our Jobs" countered highway billboards in the north coast counties. "Save the Redwoods—For Tall Dogs" sneered a bumper sticker graffito. Several lumber company offices were picketed by placard-carrying members of a student group called Active Conservation Tactics.

As an emotional fog settled around the redwoods, author-ecologist Raymond Dasmann spoke for most observers when he said, "It is getting difficult to separate sense from nonsense in the reams of material that have been written for and against the national park."

Coldly and simply, the millions of words said this:

PRO—Sempervirens is a resource of great beauty and inspirational value, an ancient heritage deserving of national recognition. The best of the old trees must be preserved for the enjoyment of all—now and in the future. The irreplaceable old-growth redwoods in private hands will be gone in twenty or thirty years. Only five of the present state parks are sizable (over eight thousand acres). If thirty thousand acres of private land were to be taken for a national park, it would be only two percent of the commercial forest acreage of the Redwood Region. Any local economic losses will eventually be compensated by increased tourism. Because of mounting pressures for public recreation, more land must be acquired by the federal government. Only federal ownership can protect the superlative groves from the highway builders.

CON—The best of the redwoods have been saved, else why would all national park plans require the taking over of one or more state parks? With the exception of the grove of tallest trees already dedicated to free public use under private ownership, the park would add little of value to the 145,000 acres of existing reserves. The additional thirty thousand acres, remote and largely inaccessible, would confiscate more than ten percent of the privately owned old-growth timber badly needed by the redwood industry for its transition to a young-growth, sustained-yield economy. It would also remove from production land capable of growing thirty million board feet of timber every year. That productivity is also part of our national heritage and the exclusive, alternative use means waste of a valuable natural resource. Neither the one thousand jobless workers and their families nor local taxpayers should be expected to make personal sacrifices for a park whose need has not been demonstrated. About nine percent of all California land is now dedicated to public recreation and further federal acquisitions in remote areas are questionable.

Three years after Dr. Zahl's discovery, the conservation movement was embroiled in factional campaigning that suggested a campus popularity contest transferred to the political scene. The administration's Mill Creek proposal picked up endorsements from the Save-the-Redwoods League, the Izaak Walton League, then-Governor Edmund G. Brown, and the California Park Commission. Lining up behind the twice-as-large Redwood Creek proposal, known as the Sierra Club bill, were the Garden Clubs of America, the Wilderness Society, the Audubon Society, the National Parks Association, and other groups.

The industry-backed Redwood Park and Recreation Plan, though not in the legislative hopper, received the endorsement of twenty-one thousand petition-signers and more than one hundred local and regional organizations.

Representative Clausen's Redwoods-to-the-Sea bill was endorsed by local government agencies, several Congressmen, the California Wildlife Federation, and a number of service clubs in the affected area.

The American Forestry Association dropped its own ill-fated plan and decided to support the administration proposal, though it later switched allegiance to the Clausen bill.

The unclear battle lines were obscured by the statements, resolutions, advertisements, and press releases of interested parties. Partisans accused each other of trying to put "the wrong park in the wrong place."

"We have fallen back," sighed a former chief of the U.S. Forest Service, "into the propaganda method of creating national parks."

New organizations were added to the list of combatants, though their names didn't always indicate their position. The Redwood Park and Recreation Committee was opposed to the objectives of Citizens for Regional Recreation and Parks. The Redwoods-to-the-Sea Committee did not share the viewpoints of the Emergency Committee for the Redwoods. Students for Redwood Creek and Citizens for a Redwood National Park both took the Sierra Club line.

A bewildered public, unfamiliar with the difference between Redwood Creek, Mill Creek, Little Lost Man Creek, Bull Creek, or the hundred miles of redwoods in between could well have believed that since all parks are good, the biggest must be the best.

Interior Secretary Stewart Udall in the fall of 1966 asked the Miller-Rellim companies to halt logging on all their lands, being considered under the administration Mill Creek's proposal. Miller refused, claiming that this would mean shutting down his operation and firing three hundred employees. Why, he asked, was his firm singled out when at least three other companies were logging in areas that were being considered under different park bills?

Senator Thomas Kuchel of California, primary backer of the administration bill, accused the company of "spite cutting," and introduced an unusual bill that would have imposed a fine of fifty thousand dollars a day on Miller for logging its own trees. All persons taking part would be jailed three months for each day's violation.

The people of Del Norte County, fearful of a Mill Creek park that would shut down their leading commercial enterprise and bring economic hardships, turned out three thousand strong for a protest rally and started a phone and mail campaign among their friends across the nation. Borrowing a tactic from preservation activists, they paraded before TV cameras with placards opposing the Administration plan. The county's population of eighteen thousand people in one day dumped fourteen thousand telegrams of protest on Congress.

Chairman Henry Jackson of the Senate interior committee watched the mounting pressures and growing disagreement among park advocates. He persuaded Miller as well as the principals of four other companies to voluntarily subscribe to a cutting moratorium that more reasonably applied only to key areas covered by the redwood park bills then in the hopper.

In order to get the redwood national park started, an impatient President Lyndon B. Johnson announced he would appropriate ten million dollars from the Land and Water Conservation Fund. The unprecedented gesture of generosity was, the Bureau of the Budget reminded the President, not exactly legal. Only Congress can appropriate from the fund and that body was nowhere near making up its mind on which of three or four types of park it wanted.

The affected redwood companies dropped their opposition to the principle of a national park and took the united stand that if Congress and the people wanted a park, then it should be one that "will not significantly harm other people by removing their jobs, tax-supported services, and the timber supply that supports them."

It appeared that no matter where the musical parks game

ended, the area would lose about a billion board feet of commercial timber. And on the usual basis that each dollar in stumpage value generates an additional twenty-five dollars' worth of derived goods and services, that meant an immediate economic loss of one billion dollars or more. It would wipe out an estimated five hundred primary jobs and another seven hundred dependent jobs.

Just before the fall elections of 1967, the Senate passed its redwood national park bill, S.2515, authored by Senators Jackson and Kuchel. Hailed as a compromise, it had taken some of the administration bill, a large part of the Sierra Club bill, and combined them with all of the Clausen bill's northern unit to make a sixty-four-thousand-acre park in two counties. Cost: $100 million.

The administration's plan to provide in-lieu tax payments for hard-hit local government agencies was dropped. In its place appeared a hotly debated provision to trade thirteen thousand acres of the federally owned Northern Redwood Purchase Unit with private companies. This would place the timberland back on local tax rolls, the Senate report argued, easing the economic hardship and, incidentally, lowering the cash cost of the park by tens of millions of dollars.

While the Purchase Unit was administered by the U.S. Forest Service, it had never been part of a national forest. In bits and pieces, its nine hundred million board feet of redwood timber was acquired from private owners in the Depression and World War II years. The mountainous area is unsuitable for either park or preservation purposes, government agencies agree.

Trading federal forest land with private owners is a common practice throughout the country, designed to block up intermingled holdings to the advantage of both parties. Except for previous trades to protect rare Sierra redwoods from logging, the Department of Agriculture's national forest holdings had never been swapped to acquire land for park purposes. The issue brought an open split between the secretaries of Interior and Agriculture.

The Sierra Club supported Interior's National Park Service on the trade. Eight major national conservation groups sided with Agriculture's Forest Service, claiming a precedent that would endanger the integrity of the national forests. The timber industry expressed divided opinions.

In mid-summer of 1967, Georgia-Pacific Corp. began construction of a moratorium-delayed access road several miles south of the tall trees area and started selective logging on the hillsides of McArthur Creek, a half-dozen miles to the northwest. Neither activity was carried on within the boundaries of the Senate-passed bill, the company claimed. But the areas might be included later by the House, charged the Sierra Club.

Full-page advertisements blossomed in newspapers across the country. The Sierra Club accused G-P of cutting inside the boundaries of a future park and practicing "legislation by chain saw." The besieged firm called the club's charges "lies, distortions, and innuendoes." Both parties threatened lawsuits.

The Jackson-Kuchel bill came before the House committee on national parks early in 1968. Its chairman, Wayne Aspinall of Colorado, was among those who received the bill coolly. Money for acquiring national parks comes primarily from the Land and Water Conservation Fund, whose income from recreation-user fees, pleasure-boat fuel taxes, and sale of surplus federal property was not meeting its expenditures. There were at least two hundred park projects ahead of the redwood bill, Aspinall explained, and a one-hundred-million-dollar tap at this time would have stopped the financing of any other park for ten years.

The House committee in mid-1968 sawed the Senate's park bill in half—to twenty-eight-thousand acres—and slipped it quickly through a floor vote under suspension of the rules. Aspinall was severely criticized by park proponents for "selling out to the selfish lumber interests."

The Colorado Congressman was working for a larger redwood park in his own way as the prime mover in a successful effort to earmark $200 million a year from federal offshore-oil revenues for the Conservation Fund. When that bill passed, a large redwood park for the first time became financially feasible.

A joint conference committee smoothed out the differences between House and Senate versions, kept the trade provision, and settled on a fifty-eight-thousand-acre park costing ninety-two million dollars for acquisition. The bill passed easily. House Speaker John W. McCormack gave it most of the credit for his being able to call the 90th Congress the "most historic" in conservation achievements.

President Johnson signed the Redwood National Park Act at White House Ceremonies in October, 1968, admitting that he had never been in the redwoods.

With a stroke of his pen, the President created an instant national park in the valley of Redwood Creek and somewhat uncertainly bracketed in three state parks and a county beach park. It placed the federal label on a long, irregularly shaped strip of ocean beaches, lagoons, and timberland that showcases many of the good features of all the redwood country. For fifty miles, the Redwood Highway wanders through the nation's longest ocean front park, taking the motorist from Jedediah Smith Redwoods State Park, near the Oregon border, southward through Crescent City, the Del Norte Coast Redwoods State Park, and across the Klamath River to Prairie Creek Redwoods State Park. Just above the town of Orick, the federal boundary detours to the south to include the ham-shaped Redwood Creek unit. Before the federal-state park complex ends at Dry Lagoon Beach State Park, twenty-five miles north of Eureka, the visitor has had the opportunity to enjoy Stout Grove and the largest-known redwood, the Prairie Creek elk herd, scenic Fern Canyon, the timbertopped cliffs of Gold Bluff Beach, the tallest trees, thirty-three miles of ocean beaches, and thirty-two thousand acres of oldgrowth forests.

Outside the state parks, a total of 30,532 acres of private land was included in the boundaries, primarily in the Redwood Creek area. A 2,700-acre unit connecting Jedediah Smith and Del Norte Coast parks was picked up in the Mill Creek Basin. An unspecified area of 2,431 acres may be located wherever the Secretary of the Interior chooses in the future.

Four timber-products firms were hardest hit by the acquisitions, their long-range sustained-yield plans crippled, at least temporarily. Arcata Redwood Company, with three hundred employees, gave up eleven thousand acres and seventy percent of its timber.

Local officials blame the park for an immediate loss of tax revenue amounting to at least $500,000 a year. Predictably, Humboldt County in 1969 raised its timberland assessments one hundred percent over the 1968 rate.

"The new park ends a long controversy," said Paul Cox of the State Division of Forestry, "and begins several new ones."

For the first time, private land was acquired for a national park through the legislative declaration-of-taking process. This meant an instant transfer of title to the government. The 120 different owners of the 28,201 acres specified in the act will be paid six percent annual interest until they receive full compensation.

Instead of the customary arbitration of confiscated land values in a district court, the matter of how much some of the private land was worth on October 2, 1969, will be decided eventually by the U.S. Court of Claims in Washington, D.C. All parties agree that it will be a matter of years before trading arrangements and final cash settlements are made.

Some government officials unofficially share the concern of local citizens that the original estimates for buying land, made hurriedly at Congressional request, may be too low. In the year between Senate passage of the park bill and signing by the President, the value of timber stumpage all along the Pacific Coast rose from twenty-five to one hundred percent. The last acquisition estimate made by the Park Service in the region—fourteen million dollars for the lagging Point Reyes National Seashore project—has since proved to be three hundred percent short.

For some years in the future, visitors to the federally owned areas will find none of the campgrounds or facilities common to other national parks. Congress has been slow in providing the requested funds for operation and development, forcing overnight patrons to seek accommodations outside the land under federal control.

Among other continuing difficulties is the matter of which government agencies will control and maintain the network of public and private roads lacing the national park. One company alone has thirteen major logging roads running through the fifty-mile-long reservation. If log trucks and other commercial vehicles are to be kept outside the park for aesthetic reasons, the alternative may be the building of substitute roads at taxpayer expense.

The Congressional report accompanying the bill and the subsequent Redwood National Park Act presumes donation of three state-owned parks. The California Constitution prohibits such donations, however, and the legislature, which can change the law, has opposed redwood national park proposals in 1947, 1963, and 1965, specifically condemning any federal park that would take over state parks without compensation at fair market value. Acting on a suggestion first made in 1965 by director George Hartzog of the National Park Service, state officials have said they will accept trades of park-quality land owned by the Interior Department elsewhere in California, though no one knows the location of tradable federal property worth the estimated quarter-billion-dollar market value of the three state parks.

"You may be sure," says State Parks Director William Penn Mott, "we're not going to give away our parks."

While the State of California continues to manage its share of the hyphenated federal-state-county park, there is a scurrying to unsnarl the red tape binding the national park package. Governor Reagan has appointed a Special Study Commission to investigate transfer of state parks. The federal Department of Housing and Urban Development has granted funds for a two-year, park-related survey of land use planning in four North Coast counties. Arcata Redwood Co. has put up $100,000 for a local economic development study. The Park Service has appointed a Master Plan team of civil service officials and leading citizens to work on management and development programs "to harmonize with existing realities and needs of the surrounding communities."

Another potentially troublesome feature of the Redwood National Park Act is the power given to the Secretary of the Interior to control logging, road-building, and resort development near, but at unspecified distances outside the park boundaries. This would be done by securing legal easements in order to protect watershed and scenic values. In the Redwood Creek watershed alone, this provision could apply to more than two hundred square miles.

There are some who think that while Public Law 90-545 represents the best compromise available, the nation may have made a poor bargain. State Park Commissioner Margaret Owings complains that federal acquisition of the specified 28,128 private acres produced a net gain of about 320 acres of redwoods classified as the superlative type. A lumberman further questioned the quality of the park since the Redwood Creek area had never been considered in the park acquisition plans of either the state or the Save-the-Redwoods League.

A tragic aftermath of the Johnson Administration's impatience is revealed by Leo Rennert, Washington correspondent for the McClatchy Newspapers, who links the national park with the devastating pollution of the Santa Barbara Channel by oil in 1969. There's little disagreement that the oil slick was caused by improper federal safeguards against oil drilling leaks. The regulations were only about one-third as effective as those applied by the State of California before the federal takeover, Governor Reagan charged.

In the rush to secure offshore oil revenues for the Land and Water Conservation Fund so that the faltering redwood national park bill could be passed before Congressional adjournment, the Secretary of the Interior brushed aside protests of local officials and authorized immediate drilling in federal lands outside the three-mile limit, Rennert reported.

"Like Faust's legendary pact," he said, "a deal which seemed so right and promising at first had ended up by exacting a terrible price."

Leaking oil killed waterfowl, seals, fishlife, and whales within an eight-hundred-square-mile area off the southern California coast. Physical damage costs were counted in the millions.

It was no accidental disaster, Rennert concluded, the blame being shared by the former Secretary of the Interior, "and, yes, even the leading conservation club."

Creating a national park does not end the war in the redwoods. Congress still considers bills that would extend the park by adding private timberlands on both sides of the Redwood Highway in the Skunk Cabbage Creek, Bald Ridge, and Redwood Creek areas. The president of the Sierra Club has announced a continuing campaign for acquiring another twenty-thousand acres of tree farms.

Memories of the long, bitter campaign were put aside on a misty day during 1968's Thanksgiving week, when local residents turned out to welcome Mrs. Lyndon B. Johnson with traditional North Coast hospitality. From a point overlooking Redwood Creek, since named Lady Bird Hill, the First Lady dedicated the nation's thirty-fourth national park.

"This is the crowning moment of a crusade which has lasted for generations," she said. "Now the dream of conservationists and nature lovers is a reality for all the people. The California redwood trees are now a permanent part of the nation's heritage."

Chapter XII

*Forest Playground*

Come and enjoy our redwoods, say the warmhearted people of the region, smugly certain that they live in the greatest scenery factory in the world.

The invitation is issued sincerely—for now, at least—with only the slightest trace of foreboding. This is an area where it may not be too late to apply the lessons of recreational popularity that have brought ugliness and management scandals to forested playgrounds and national parks elsewhere.

The region is vulnerable. About ninety percent of it is relatively untouched by the unpleasant crunch of 1,500 people who join California's population each day or the nationwide increase of twenty percent in recreationist numbers each year. But better roads are coming.

Most of the fifteen counties of the Redwood Region are joined like shish kebab on an asphalt skewer of highway that begins with Monterey County's State 1—first unit of a future statewide scenic roadway system—drifts northward into ridge-running Skyline Boulevard of the San Francisco Peninsula, and becomes the 350-mile-long Redwood Highway from the Golden Gate into Oregon.

These arteries of commerce also carry an increasing flow of tourists and recreationists who have learned that in the northern California coast country there's still room enough to get lost. This is the dampest part of California, but it is still California; there are enough pleasant summer days to make the area's promotability envied by chambers of commerce elsewhere.

"What you like to do most, you can do best in the Redwood Empire" crows the tourist-boosting Redwood Empire Association. Though one man's idea of recreation may be another's poison oak, the great variety of the landscape offers something for everyone. California's coastal counties are essentially snow-free, with a Mediterranean-like climate, and recreational opportunities span the calendar.

Surveys show that most travelers on the redwooded highways are scenery inspectors, and they are well rewarded. But more active recreationists, from abalone fishermen to wildflower gatherers, have equal advantages.

The main reason, natural attractions aside, is availability. Government agencies control about one of each four acres in the region and two of every three acres of forest land. Except for parks it is open to recreationists without charge.

To visitors from less-favored sections of the country, one of the most unusual things about the region is a pleasant remnant of its frontier hospitality, the large amount of private forest land available to the recreation-seeker.

**REDWOOD INDUSTRY RECREATION AREAS**

Leading this movement is the Redwood Industry Recreation Areas program. It began in 1965, when nine timber companies joined to open some of their forest lands under the overall sponsorship of the California Redwood Association. There are uniform policies, regulations, signboards, and literature. An advisory committee is composed of representatives of the Izaak Walton League, California Wildlife Federation, and other land-using organizations.

The twenty-five RIRA areas in Mendocino, Humboldt, and Del Norte counties embrace old- and young-growth forests, mountains, lagoons, and several miles of ocean beaches. There are four hundred miles of fishing streams.

Fun down on the tree farm began with the opening of gates on 260,000 acres of commercial forest. Past experience across the country showed that the landowner might also be opening his gates to trouble. Sign shooting, littering, and equipment theft were some of the lesser evils. More worrisome were the dangers that have been responsible for delaying public access to private land everywhere: road damage, legal liability of the owner for recreationist injury or death, and—most important—fire.

When the first year came and went with no serious problems, the RIRA welcome mat in the woods was extended to 365,000 acres. As recreationist guests continued to mind their outdoor manners, more land was opened and it now approaches the 400,000-acre level.

About 150,000 recreational visits are recorded each year.

Almost all of this acreage is wildland. It helps fill the recreational gap between the primitive, less-accessible national forest offerings and the electrified comforts of resorts and state park campgrounds. Its fishing and hunting attractions help bring sportsmen to the north coast outside the three-month "rubber-necking" season.

Overnight, CRA says, the nine companies created a new outdoor playground equal in area to all the national forests in Indiana, Iowa, Kansas, Maine, Massachusetts, New York, and Ohio. It is at least three times the size of California's coast redwood park system and allows many of the recreational pursuits—hunting, berry picking, dog running, and the incidental gathering of driftwood and rocks—that are denied visitors in government parks.

The foresters who manage the program on the ground are far from displeased that they must divert some of their attention from the business of growing trees to coping with the inevitable nuisances and new problems of accommodating the public. Some are enthusiastic, pointing out that RIRA is, after all, merely an extension of the principle they learned from forestry textbooks: getting the maximum productivity of all values from a given area of land.

Sponsors of the program believe this merging of public and private interests is the only solution to the rising conflict in demand for tangible benefits of the forest—jobs, products, and tax-supported services—as well as the demand for recreation and scenery.

The unusual cooperative program has received an award for good forest management from the National Forest Products Association. It could be a model for public recreation on private land elsewhere in the nation.

Fees? For now, at least, the only price recreationists are asked to pay is alertness and consideration.

That means care with fire, for example. When the humidity drops to thirty percent in the late summer and early fall, and the timber is dry, land managers cross their fingers and perform a subliminal rain dance. The average cost of putting out a forest fire in the north coast is fifty thousand dollars—timber and watershed losses apart. State law requires the closing of both government and private forests to logging and recreational use when conditions become dangerous. The locked gates are a guarantee that the recreational attractions of the land, as well as its timber, will be protected for future use, though the thought is sometimes difficult to convey to the frustrated hunter holding an unused deer tag on the last day of the hunting season.

The forests are also closed year-round in areas where logging takes place. The private roads here are narrow, and ten-foot-wide log trucks, burdened by twenty or thirty tons, may be using either side of the road in following rules designed for the safety of workers and equipment rather than recreational visitors.

The popularity of mechanized deer hunting has brought another restriction in many parks and recreation areas, where hunters' motorcycles and other small vehicles must be kept out because of fire hazards. The road-rutting, narrow tires of these hunting bikes can also cause erosion problems.

California offers no better hunting country. The Department of Fish and Game credits past logging in the region with creating improved conditions for Roosevelt elk, black bear, rabbits, and other game animals and bringing the deer population to an all-time high.

Because most of the foods preferred by wildlife are light-loving plants, there are few animals in the virgin redwood forest, which President Ira N. Gabrielson of the Wildlife Management Institute has likened to a "biological desert." There are few insects and almost no birds.

When trees are removed by either selective or clear-cut logging, browse and forage plants quickly move in, followed by big game, grouse, band-tailed pigeon, quail, and other wildlife. For deer and elk, this "edge" condition disappears in twenty or thirty years when the young redwoods grow tall enough to shade out the brush. But logging continues nearby and the game moves, assuring a permanently high population of wildlife unknown in past centuries.

The old logging roads and trails lacing the forest make it easier going for recreationists and, more important from a game management standpoint, disperse hunters for more uniform cropping of animals.

The recently logged redwood forest is probably the best deer nursery in the nation, producing an average of four or five blacktails to the acre for a period of many years. Humboldt and Mendocino counties, by no coincidence, perenially come up with the state's highest lumber output as well as the highest bag of deer.

The region is notable fishing country too, with a diverse menu that includes clams, crabs, abalones, surf fish, cod, rock fish, and salmon from the ocean, as well as rainbow, steelhead, and cutthroat trout from a hundred steams draining the redwood forests. The migratory shad and striped bass that cruise regional waters are descendants of fish from Eastern states planted here in the last century. Once in a while an angler tangles with a native sturgeon, though he'll have to throw the fish back if it's less than the keeper size of three and a half feet in length.

Less active recreationists have been flocking lately to the little excursion railroads that wander leisurely through the redwood forests. Each of the lines is powered by steam locomotives, and as an old-time woodsman said, that's the way God intended.

The Roaring Camp & Big Trees Railroad, six miles north of Santa Cruz, uses noisy geared engines to haul sightseers into the woods near Cowell State Park and upgrade to a reconstructed lumber mill town.

No reconstruction was necessary with the North Coast's beloved Skunk Line. Mills now under the Boise-Cascade Corp.

banner have been operating log and lumber railroads out of
Fort Bragg for three quarters of a century and its California
Western Railroad to this day is a working line. Railfans know
it as the only regularly scheduled standard gauge steam road
in the nation. Through forty miles of scenic regrowth redwoods, a pair of snorting steamers and a trio of yellow motor
coaches—whose gasoline odor forty years ago gave the line
its permanent nickname—carry more than 120,000 passengers a year between the coastal mill town and Willits, on
the Redwood Highway. After the day-time conductors have
worn their fingers out pointing to the scenery, the railroad
changes into overalls and hauls lumber at night.

The Klamath and Hoopow Short Line Railroad is a recent
addition to the revived woods railroads, running steam pots
into the forest from the town of Klamath on an irregular
schedule.

The Arcata & Mad River Railroad of Simpson Timber Co.
has been hauling redwood logs and lumber for 115 years, and
in 1969 reinstated passenger service from the mill town of
Blue Lake down the Mad River to its station near Arcata, using an antique Shay engine. With a feeling for the past seldom
found in modern corporations, the proprietors have honored
the workhorse who first pulled A&M trains by naming their
geared locomotive Spanking Fury.

The regional reluctance to part with its past brings another
sightseeing bonus to visitors, who are usually unaware of the
existence of six covered bridges, all built of redwood, tucked
away on little roads to nowhere. Four, including a brand new
private structure over Jacoby Creek near Arcata, carry auto
traffic.

"Newest" of the surviving public bridges is at Berta's Ranch
on the Elk River five miles south of Eureka. At thirty-two
years of age it is only six months younger than the Zane's
Ranch bridge a mile away. The Felton Bridge, one mile east
of its namesake town, was built in 1892. The seventy-seven-
year-old Glen Canyon Bridge, in Santa Cruz' Delaveaga Park,
is occasionally used by Hollywood film companies. The region's oldest "kissing bridge" crosses the San Lorenzo River at
Paradise Park four miles north of Santa Cruz. Aged ninety-
seven, it is the West's best-preserved and most picturesque example of the Victorian art of roofing rivers.

Highway travelers in the three northern counties of the region have a free attraction not found elsewhere in the country. At six roadside points, including one on the boundary of

Redwood National Park's northern unit, they are invited to park their cars, take a short walk along a woods trail, and in the process learn the elements of redwood forestry firsthand.

This is the demonstration forests program of the Redwood Region Conservation Council, sponsored by timber-products companies. Guides are available at several forests during the busy summer months, but visitors are encouraged to pick up a trail guidebook and mosey along at their own pace.

A similar informative tour may be taken without leaving the car. It winds through the Yurok Experimental Forest a few miles north of the town of Klamath. Here the U.S. Forest Service is researching various methods of redwood harvesting ranging from extremely good to extremely poor. Roadside signs tell the motorist what to look for.

To most visitors, the big recreational draw of the redwoods is sight-seeing. While nearly every turn in the road offers its photogenic charms, it is in the federal, state, district, and county parks that the large attendance records are logged, particularly near the San Francisco Bay Area.

In the twenty-nine parks classified as coast-redwood type by the State of California and now open to the public, between three and four million visitor-days will be recorded this year. Yet only one in ten park users will pay a fee for either day use or overnight camping.

Surprisingly, California's booming population increase and recreational pressures have not been reflected in attendance figures at the redwood parks. Despite the addition of about twenty thousand acres to the sixteen primary redwood units since 1963, and worldwide publicity from the national park issue, annual attendance at these parks for the last five years has remained almost constant at the 2.7 million level. As the ratio of visitor-days to population, this means the relative decline for the period is about ten percent. Visits to other types of state parks have been increasing thirty times faster.

One of the reasons given for low use figures is the lack of development in the redwood parks, a half dozen of which have no campgrounds or facilities. There is an average ratio now of one campsite for each fifty-six acres. But four out of five visitors come only for a quick look at the scenery anyway and require no facilities. Of the campers, more than half stay only one night. And about eighty percent of the year's total visits are made in the thirteen weeks of summer, many of the redwood parks closing down the rest of the year for lack of business.

To residents of the region, the apparent boycott is understandable. Summertime is fogtime, and much of the rest of the year features the light rain they like to call Oregon mist, which grows progressively heavier approaching its namesake state. There is probably no damper forest to camp in due to the redwood's habit of dripping moisture year-round to its near-surface roots.

"The prevalent fogs," explains California Parks and Recreation Director William Penn Mott, "responsible for the outstanding development of the redwood groves, are also responsible for a recreation use pattern that has been brought down to the present. This is the trip inland, away from the redwoods, to a warmer, sunnier environment."

Another factor is the location of several of the largest parks in the state's remote northwestern corner, five to eight hours' driving time from the nearest population center. A state survey shows that when recreationists travel more than four hours from home, it is done almost exclusively during long vacation periods.

Under these circumstances, park officials have been reluctant to add facilities in the redwoods when the demonstrated need is greater elsewhere. And with park-users paying back only one dollar for every three spent by the state for maintenance and operation, there's little incentive to further the losing proposition.

Looking at recreation attendance figures, it might be concluded that the state's redwood park program has been a poor investment. The opinion is unjustified. The primary purpose in acquiring these timbered areas has been to preserve the best examples of *Sequoia sempervirens* as a species. In achieving that goal, the land added to the park system has often been unsuited to the traditional objective of most other parks, which is recreation.

The State Park and Recreation Commission, however, has recently reversed its long-standing policy and now plans to spend most of its funds developing facilities in the existing parks, particularly in the redwoods, instead of acquiring more land.

The move, designed to obtain greater use of the parks, was made with some misgivings, for man of the *Homo recreationii* variety has proved to be no great gift to the redwoods.

A blind person trained in litter collecting could follow the Redwood Highway with ease. Unfortunately in this case, the bulk of recreation- and beauty-seekers are not sightless and must endure the littered garbagescape produced by others' thoughtlessness. Members of Humboldt State College's Boots and Blisters hiking society recently picked up one and a half tons of discarded paper, bottles, and cans along a six-mile stretch of U.S. 101 between Orick and Prairie Creek Redwoods State Park.

Billboards and drive-ins multiply in economic progression with the number of passing prospects. The Division of Forestry reports that most of the region's five hundred annual forest fires are caused by outsiders unfamiliar with the destructive dangers of their matches and campfires. The small marine animals in the tide pools along the North Coast shore are being studied to death by collectors, warns the Department of Fish and Game, pointing to the more accessible areas now devoid of marine life. And half the newly created state park police force of twenty men is stationed in the region, with a major assignment of keeping hippie-type squatters from overstaying their welcome.

The work of the California Coastal Scenic Redwood Road and Trails Committee will bring more tourists. It was created by the legislature to investigate a system of routes from southern Monterey County to the Oregon line. Its preliminary report recommends a five-hundred-mile main road with about a thousand miles of connecting loop roads and trails. Combined with the proposed California Riding and Hiking Trails System, the Skyline National Parkway, the State Scenic Highway System, and the State Parkway program, it offers promise for the state's two most numerous outdoor recreationists, the walkers and sight-seeing drivers.

As the new highways bring once-remote sections of redwood country closer to the San Francisco Bay Area, more and more Californians are buying land for weekend and vacation use. This fast-growing movement tends to eat away at woodlands that could provide multiple benefits for the general public, yet it brings an incidental advantage that might be called de facto preservation for it is certain that few trees will be cut on these second-home forests.

Another recreation-oriented phenomenon is the well-bankrolled resort and homesite combination. Large acreages have been developed, scenic values intact, at such locations as Shelter Cove, Sea Ranch, Timber Cove, and Brooktrails, an old lumber-mill village. Their success will no doubt encourage further developments on a large scale.

Altogether, it is estimated that about a quarter million acres of redwood forest land is now held by developers and individuals for private recreational purposes.

The sharp rise in northern California recreational activity that the State Department of Parks and Recreation predicts for the future will come primarily from water-oriented activities. Lagoons, streams, and ocean beaches will be supplemented by flood control and water supply reservoirs. Among the region's first is Ruth Reservoir, on the upper Mad River, built to supply Eureka's two new pulp mills. Most will be located just east of the redwood belt and can provide the sunnier summertime recreation mentioned by Director Mott.

To many the Redwood Region means recreation. The country has kept its attractive character with the help of steep terrain, rural land-use patterns, and a geographical spread that includes remoteness. This will change, notably in the northern sections, where new freeways will doom the casual pace of life and expose the redwoods of the 100,000th century B.C. to some of the less pleasant aspects of the twentieth century of our era.

It now seems likely that more people will also add more man-caused complications to the necessary job of preserving the redwoods.

Chapter XIII

# Hell and High Water

John Muir had said, "When we try to pick out anything by itself, we find it hitched to everything else in the universe."

In his way the naturalist was describing today's discipline of ecology, a science of survival. This is the recognition that a forest, for example, is not just a collection of trees, but a complex community of living things whose presence is influenced by soil, climate and other organisms.

Man arrived recently and has proved to be the most volatile ingredient in the ecological mix. From his earliest ventures with fire and the hunting of animals, he has been influencing the course of natural processes until he is now a dominant factor in the environment.

In Muir's beloved redwood forests, the influences have been both good and bad. Only in recent years, with the arrival of an ecological conscience, have we begun to learn the consequences of human activities.

The evidence has been accumulating slowly. By the 1960's, the scores of scientific reports and observations added up to an ominous message: The evergreen Sequoia may be on a collision course with extinction.

Two adverse forces are at work. First is the gradual drying out of the tree's habitats through ecological time. The other is a slow change, speeded by man, affecting those unique bred-in characteristics of the tree that have allowed it to adapt and survive.

146

How could the redwood, a tree of high vitality, aggressiveness, longevity, and resistance to destructive agencies suddenly face the fate of its one-time associate, the dinosaur, when it has fought off the worst threats of nature for one hundred million years? The answer is as complex as the tree's eco-system.

For any tree species to endure the centuries, it must be able to reproduce itself. Seeds are the common method. Since the redwood's past habitats have been disturbed ones, it developed a special trait that allows its seeds to grow on exposed mineral soil. In fact, it is now so specialized that its seeds will not survive where the ground has not been disturbed. If there is a normal thick litter of needles, bark and debris on the forest floor, seedlings die within a year from heat, insects, or, more commonly, disease.

Unless redwood is able to reseed immediately in forest openings, competing plant species move in.

The soil was usually kept exposed for seeds by lightning-caused wildfire. Being the most fire-resistant of conifers, the redwood was little harmed by these light, frequent blazes. In the last twenty thousand years or so, primitive man also started fires in his pursuit of animals and insects for food, or to improve range conditions.

On the benches and alluvial flats, floods have been another means of assuring the necessary disturbed soil. Almost every year, high water flows harmlessly around the trees and deposits as much as three feet of sand, gravel, and silt. It is the best sort of bed for redwood seedlings, though few other plants can survive. A feature of the lowland forest is even-aged waves of redwoods, from seedlings to giants, that are known to have been born of past floods.

Over the centuries, the ability of redwood to reproduce by seeds has been gradually weakening, it is believed. Good annual seed crops are infrequent. Viability is low. One recent study suggests that even the tree's ability to produce cones declines when fire and flood are removed.

But the redwood has another trick to keep alive. It makes up for reduced seed reproduction by sending up root and stump sprouts, and this may be the only reason the species is holding on, according to Dr. Edward C. Stone, forest ecologist on the University of California faculty. Because the sprouts begin as dormant buds beneath the bark or under ground, they too need a stimulus. Normally, there is no sprouting unless the tree falls, is cut down, injured, burned, or receives sediment around stump and roots.

The natural disturbances are also beneficial to redwoods beyond the seedling stage. Flooding and fire kill off competing plants. Like a spring tonic, the larger trees respond to the moisture and debris of a flood by adding diameter growth and sending new roots into the flood-borne layer. Adding new root platforms, the tree progressively adapts to each higher ground level.

The black, hollowed-out trunks of old trees, called goose-pens by pioneers who sometimes used them for that purpose, demonstrate that even though eighty-five percent burned away, the redwood is able to add new growth over the charcoal and survive on a slender layer of sapwood. Then there are the strange fire columns sometimes seen in the forest, looking like telephone poles with a thousand short branches stuck in them; these give evidence that the trunk alone is capable of regrowing a crown after flames have killed the limbs.

Landslides, common in the virgin forests of the Redwood Region, also provide disturbed soil and, along with fire, flood, and high erosion rates, are as much a part of the redwood environment as fog. The tree has not only learned to live with these natural disturbances, but also, in the lowland forest, has come to depend on them.

The more it adapted and compromised to survive, the more specialized sempervirens became. It is now an example of survival by isolation, developing life patterns that have freed it of competition. But overspecialization leads to extinction.

We have stopped the fires. Man can no longer live with wildfire, nor can the forest. Except for closely controlled spot-burning, it would be impossible to revive this natural management tool because fuels that have been collecting on the forest floor in recent fire-free years would probably create blazes severe enough to kill even the redwoods.

Now the dams are coming. The devastating floods that hit much of the West in December, 1964, underscored the absence of adequate flood-control facilities in California's North Coast counties.

This was flood country long before man arrived. The recurring torrents have become "devastating" only since the installation of highways, buildings, railroads, and farms in the lowlands.

Nevertheless, the dams are now necessary and they will be built soon. The California Water Plan calls for six projects on the Eel, and others on the Klamath, Trinity, Russian, Little, Van Duzen, and Mad rivers, with surplus water going to southern California.

The dams will solve one problem, but they will create others for the redwood.

When flooding and resultant siltation is curtailed, warns Dr. Peter E. Black in a National Park Service study, "It is a logical assumption that the alluvial stands are doomed." Below the dams, permanent lowering of the water table could cut off the vital source of moisture. Above the dams, permanent elevation of the water table could drown out the roots, and without sediment deposition, no new roots could be grown.

Creating new superlative groves above the dams would be difficult because of fluctuating water levels.

In the forests now in parks, the human presence has become another hindrance to redwood reproduction. As early as 1929 the state became concerned and looked into the relationships between tourists and redwood parks. It was found that understory vegetation was being damaged. Some old trees were dying. Erosion was taking place on trails and campsites. Trampling feet were packing the soil around tree roots, preventing either seeding or sprouting. These problems have since accelerated.

At Armstrong Grove State Park alone, an average of twelve old trees are killed every year by ground compaction.

It has been found that intense recreational use also kills the waves of young seedlings that follow floods. In 1955, a fence was put around a barren, heavily used section of Stephens Grove in Humboldt Redwoods State Park. With people excluded, the redwood seedlings, oxalis, and fern returned to revegetate the bare ground within five or six years.

There is an almost universal belief, says a Humboldt State College study, that eventually human-use impact can become so heavy and continuous as to impair the health of the big redwoods. There is, however, no evidence of damage to trees by recreationists in young-growth or slope forests.

A further tilting of the scales of the redwood's forest ecosystem occurs with the absence of fire and flood. That is the largely unknown effects of disrupting the flow of such soil elements as phosphorous and nitrogen needed for tree growth.

The absence of fire throughout the two forests, and the

pressure of people and elimination of floods in the lowland forest, in themselves pose serious threats to the redwood's future. But the ecologists greatest concern is based on what they call the theories of plant succession and plant potential.

When the disturbances the redwood now depends upon are removed, then nature—said to be a hater of vacuums—will replace the tree with something else. In many cases, redwood is not the climax species of the land on which it grows. The eventual successors, it was long ago ordained, are hemlock, western red cedar, Douglas fir, or hardwoods. These species have been kept at bay by fire, which Muir called the master controller of the distribution of trees. The dense shade of the redwood forest has also contributed to exclusion of the redwood's sun-loving competitors. Then there's high water and sediment, tolerated by few other trees.

When natural disturbances are controlled, as in a park situation, the redwoods topple from old age, as they always have. They usually pull their root crowns over with them, making sprouting difficult. Reseeding is equally chancy. So instead of vigorous young sprouts or seedlings coming along to fill the gaps, other conifers or any of several hardwoods appear. They are able to enter now that sunlight is breaking through the overhead canopy once occupied by the dead redwood.

Tragically, the danger is greatest in lowland groves, where the stands grow purest, tallest, largest, and oldest, and were thought safe in parks. The past half century of experience and research, reads a statement from the Society of American Foresters, has provided "substantial evidence" that reservation of superlative redwoods in park status is no guarantee of their preservation.

UC redwood specialist Dr. Paul Zinke says that "by the very act of preserving these old trees, and setting aside recreational areas and state parks, we may have been signing their death warrants." Ecologist D. W. Cooper of the UC Agricultural Extension Service credits "those misguided people who propose to put more redwoods behind the fences of parks" with "asking the nation to watch the species become extinct."

The gloomy forecasts are based on the knowledge that the redwood, like other life-forms, loses vigor as it gets older. A UC study showed that seeds become progressively less able to germinate as the tree ages until 1,200 years, when they are usually sterile. The ability to grow new trees by sprouting also declines with age and size, and often disappears after six hundred years. While ninety percent of trees in the forty-inch size sprout when they're felled or damaged, it happens to only half those of nine-foot diameter or larger.

There's trouble ahead, too, in the limited spread of tree ages in the lowland groves. "If we assume the redwood's average life span to be 500 or 700 years," says Dr. Stone, "our children's children's children are going to be viewing a pretty sorry spectacle, unless we can begin to set aside today some younger age classes."

In California's most northerly park groves, the redwoods that pioneer Jedediah Smith knew, will be replaced by hemlock, according to Dr. Walter C. Lowdermilk's report to the Save-the-Redwoods League. Other successors in the northern range may be cedar, laurel, or red alder. Elsewhere, tan oak, madrona, white fir, and Douglas fir are among the trees whose seeds can grow where redwoods' cannot.

Outside the lowland groves, the million and a half acres of the slope forest is in less danger. The trees here do not rely on flood and silt. Interruption of the nitrogen cycle in the soil is less evident. Being younger and smaller, the trees reproduce effectively. Nevertheless, the absence of fire, if nothing else, is expected to eventually eliminate the upland forests in parks and reserves. Their remaining life is more likely to be measured in thousands of years, however, instead of the scores or hundreds left to the unmanaged lowland forest.

Ironically, the place where the redwood is safest of all from man's ecological tampering is in the commercial forest. Most of the land is privately owned and about one million acres is under long-term forest management. Here, such activities as logging, grazing, road building, and slash burning artificially create some of the rough-and-tumble conditions that ecological studies have shown the redwood needs for natural reproduction and survival. The requirements of mineral soil, access to light, and lessened competition are provided.

How soon the lowland redwoods will be replaced by competing trees depends on how long they can maintain their vitality in a man-changed environment. If the nitrogen cycle of the soil has been blocked, the end could come as soon as a hundred years, Dr. Stone suggests. In other cases, he believes, it may be many centuries.

A classic principle of plant succession has been summed up by Leslie M. Reid, head of the Department of Recreation and Parks at Texas A & M University, who states that any organism has only three choices when faced by a hostile or lethal change in environmental conditions: to migrate, to mutate, or to die. For sempervirens, boxed in along a foggy coastal strip, the migrating days are over. Its strange and unique adaptations to its present environment have taken a hundred million years to develop, and any further mutations or sudden changes in its odd chromosome structure seem unlikely. Some scientists believe we are selective-breeding the most desirable traits out of the tree.

Nature's harsh third choice, death, appears inevitable to several of the dozen or so specialists studying the redwood's eco-system. They say that no matter what we do now, no matter how much we might wish for its survival, the tree is doomed.

Dr. William C. Steere, director of the New York Botanical Garden, puts the blame primarily on a gradually drying climate. Almost unnoticed, the moisture that nature allots to northern California has been slowly diminishing. This trend has been observed on some upland forests where the redwood finds it difficult to reproduce on drier slopes. In the critical month of August, it generally requires at least three or four times more moisture than Douglas fir, madrona, and tan oak.

Dr. Stephen H. Spurr of the University of Michigan is among those who claim that plant succession is inevitable, "and no human jailer or preservationist can prevent it."

Others hope that by drastically changing our resource-management policies we can keep the tree alive until science finds measures to counter the hostile forces.

"Time is running out for the alluvial flat redwoods because of man's interference," warns Dr. Stone. "It is too late to achieve preservation without man's counter-interference. Managed manipulation is the only solution."

The first step, all agree, is to protect young seedlings and the roots of old trees from damage by recreationists. In some state parks, heavily used trails and camping areas are being layered with wood chips to prevent compaction of the soil, though visitors have been known to gather the material for burning in their campfires.

The National Park Service has announced plans to control visitors by means of a motorized "elephant train" that will

haul them in comfort into Redwood Creek Valley. Some preservationists, however, feel the bus line would be a jarring in-
trusion akin to a Disneyland concession in the Sistine Chapel.

Further protection of the endangered old-growth groves
will come with the moving of recreational developments to
higher ground or into young-growth forests. Automobile
roads should avoid the best trees. Heavily used areas should
be rotated.

Park patrons might put up with such inconveniences if the
situation is explained to them, but other measures that now
seem necessary to save the best groves will not be received
warmly.

Floods, for example. The major watersheds of the region
are as good as dammed by the water planners. In smaller watersheds, there is still a chance to maintain the natural "disas-
ters" that will extend the life expectancy of the lowland redwoods. Though park visitors may not think too highly of
walking through three feet of last winter's silt, Dr. Black opti-
mistically points out that the floods do bring the advantage of
wiping away all traces of previous human use.

There's some hope offered by a recently concluded
five-year study made by UC's Wildland Research Center in
cooperation with the State Department of Parks and Recreation. It began as an investigation of the impact of freeways on
the redwoods. But when the highway-building threat was removed, the survey was broadened to consider all ecological
factors.

Some of the preliminary conclusions made in the yet-
unreleased report:

To perpetuate the redwood, some disturbance is essential.
To carry on present park-management policies threatens to
destroy the very trees we are trying to save.

Natural regeneration of the type that follows logging on
the industrial forests, supplemented by artificial replanting
and reseeding where necessary, is the best management practice now known to assure perpetuation of the species. It must
not, however, be carried on in a manner that will permanently damage soil and watershed values.

In a few cases, such as the fire-ravaged fir forest land of
the upper Bull Creek Basin, intensive manipulation of the entire watershed may be necessary to maintain downstream redwoods.

Better coordination of all resource development, a sort of

total management concept including planning, construction, and operation of facilities, is needed on a regional basis. This applies to agriculture, highway building, mining, business and residential developments, recreation, timber, range, wildlife, fisheries, and water resources.

The park manager will have to substitute for nature and on both lowland and slope forests get rid of the plants that will move in with the crippling of the redwood's eco-system. That means either selective logging the invaders, killing them with herbicides, burning periodically, or some combination of these steps.

Another recent study made by Dr. T. N. Stoate at the Simpson Timber Co. soils laboratory suggests that seedlings growing in ground that has not been burned, flooded, or mechanically disturbed may be protected by artificially sterilizing the soil to prevent the otherwise inevitable death from disease.

The missing flow of mineral elements needed by the tree, lost when fires and floods are prevented, might be recreated by means of artificial fertilization—a sort of underground vitamin pill—according to one hopeful ecologist.

All scientific studies and conclusions now indicate that the type of overprotective, roll-back-the-clock nonmanagement suitable for parks elsewhere is not going to work in the redwoods. Here, the new tools of the park manager will be the chain saw, the bulldozer, herbicides, fire, chemicals, and a large supply of Keep Out signs.

"True preservation of the superlative groves," concurs the Northern California Section of the Society of American Foresters, "must consist, in effect, of managing change."

The people studying the redwood and its environment precede all their observations with the familiar scientific disclaimer that more research is needed. It will take another five or ten years, for example, before enough data is available to predict the climax association—those tree species or combinations destined to replace redwood on specific lowland groves.

Meanwhile, there's no question that we have severely disrupted the redwood's eco-system and are now experimenting —right or wrong—with the best of the remaining groves. Children of floods, they were created almost cataclysmically, Dr. Zinke says, and that may well be the way they'll end.

The State Department of Parks and Recreation has become aware of the dangers in the old preservation concept.

Campgrounds are quietly being moved out of the old forests. Some compacted tree roots are being removed with the aid of bulldozers. In the Sierra redwood state parks fire is being used experimentally to improve natural regeneration and might later be applied to sempervirens. The Coast Redwood Park Master Plan, issued in 1965, called for the addition of forty-five thousand acres to existing parks, of which only sixty-five hundred acres was to be old growth. The remaining acreage would be not only more attractive for recreation, it was stated, but better suited for perpetuation management.

While all citizens share the deep feeling of preservationists that some areas of the earth must be left untouched by man, Dean Zivnuska believes that in the redwoods the opportunity no longer exists. Natural forces cannot be stopped by a park fence. The look of always is an unattainable dream.

Nor is it possible anywhere, states Dr. Glenn T. Seaborg, chairman of the Atomic Energy Commission. "We cannot return to a primitive state to retain our planet unspoiled and unsullied. It is possible for civilized man to coexist with nature. It is not an 'either/or' situation. A rational man can both enjoy and use his environment."

It is far more important, believe Dr. Steere and others, to maintain a plant species for future generations than to make an all-out effort to preserve populations of interesting or spectacular species "when they are actually living fossils marked for eventual extinction by nature herself through long-term normal changes."

Despite the unpleasant evidence, there may be time to apply what little we have learned so far to prolong the life of the remarkable redwood, to further the incessant journey known as the development process. The object should be to perpetuate the species both in the outdoor museum groves and in the commercial forests, say the ecologists. And that's going to take some drastic changes not only in land-management techniques, but in the public's attitudes and governmental policies. The challenge may be as much to recreationists and admirers of the redwoods as it is to professional resource managers.

# Chapter XIV

## *Forest Frontier*

Through the ages, nature has come up with a strange series of little miracles designed to maintain the redwood amid an ever-changing natural environment.

Inventor Thomas Edison sensed the phenomenon in a 1926 visit, when he said, "The reason for the great longevity of this species is that here there has been a perfect balance between the redwood tree and all or nearly all surrounding conditions."

The ancient balance has been upset. Man's influence has automatically usurped the management of the tree. If there is a future for sempervirens, it is now almost entirely in our hands.

In our complex society, we have added a number of economic and social pressures to the management of our natural resources that in the case of the redwood act like an extension of its own eco-system. To the laws of nature we have added artificial laws in the form of public policies.

Though all these expressions of the public will are well intended, serving some useful purpose, they are usually applied unilaterally, without coordination with other policies and with little concern for side effects. The result in the field of resource management is comparable to tampering with one of the vital life processes of the redwood without compensating with artificial substitute measures.

There are dozens of accumulated policies that now affect the redwoods, for good or evil. Among them are such diverse influences as flood control, highway routing, fish and game laws, minimum wages, foreign trade, land zoning, and fire control.

On the 1.4 million acres of redwoods privately owned, taxation is an important player in the policy game. Both the land and the trees are taxed at the county and district level. Profits from the sale of timberland are taxed at the state and federal level. The rate of this taxation can determine the quality of forest practices.

In the last century, many operators skinned off the redwoods as quickly as possible, as they had in the East, letting the land revert to the county for nonpayment of taxes. Though the U.S. Forest Service as early as 1903 had pointed out that it pays to hold logged-off redwood lands for future crops "under favorable conditions," a few land-skinners were still around until after World War I.

Following the pioneering declaration of the large redwood landowners that they intended to grow trees on a permanent basis, the people of California in 1926 were presented with a proposed amendment to the state constitution. It provided that owners of cutover forest land may choose not to pay taxes on the new crop of timber until it is forty years old or more. Normal land taxes would still have to be paid. The owner would apply for the timber tax exemption and have his land inspected by a Timber Maturity Board to determine its qualification. Strongly backed by the legislature, the press and conservation groups, the measure passed and is still in effect.

The carrying charges, or total cost of maintaining the land and timber for the next crop of trees, was lowered to a reasonable level by the amendment, landowners could afford to farm trees, and the overall effect has unquestionably been in the public interest.

Whether the law can keep up with changing conditions, including the possibility that redwoods less than forty years of age can be thinned and utilized in new products, is being investigated by the Society of American Foresters, the California Forest Protective Association, and several counties.

Another state tax policy is having an opposite effect from the 1926 law on those landowners with permanent forest-management programs. It is the requirement that all land of similar type be assessed equally, regardless of its use. In application, it means that the one acre of forest land bought for one thousand dollars by a city dweller for his summer cabin brings nearby industrial forest land under consideration for like value, and it may be reassessed on that basis. In some areas, the resultant boost in taxes has forced landowners to take their land out of timber production and develop it for resort or residential uses, or to cut the timber in order to get out from under the tax burden.

As more vacationers and retirees run to the forested areas for escape from urban pressures and each other, taxation threatens the redwoods with the same fate as the dwindling orchards of Santa Clara Valley, the citrus groves of Los Angeles County, and the "wood ranches" that once surrounded Lake Tahoe. In recent years, the average assessment of private timber per thousand board feet has more than doubled in Humboldt County and risen throughout the region.

There's some hope in California's new agricultural reserve and open space laws, though their effect will not be felt for some years. They are intended to keep unimproved land productive of both crops and scenery by granting tax relief to cooperating livestock growers, ranchers, and tree farmers.

At the federal level, Congress in 1944 passed a law that permits timber revenues to be taxed at a twenty-five-percent capital-gains rate rather than forty-eight percent, treating timber like any other real estate. The object is the same as the California law—to encourage good forestry and to prevent bad cutting practices. It is not related to the oil industry's depletion allowance, which is a cost allowance rather than a modified tax on income. Yet nearly every session of Congress hears attacks on the complex provision, inspired by an understandable, but mistaken belief that it represents some type of special privilege.

"The North Coast region has a very strong stake in terms of its total economy in the maintenance of capital gains for timber," says Dean Zivnuska. But in common with other tax laws designed to improve forestry, "this will require some explaining to the public" if its importance is to be understood and the laws maintained.

With the help of equitable tax laws, timberland ownership has stabilized. There is no such thing as cut-out and get-out in the mid-twentieth century. Now that circumstances have changed, some suggest that the laws be changed. Since trees are now a crop, shouldn't the taxes that now tend to encourage premature cutting be eliminated and timber be treated equally with other produce of the land?

Other public pressures, seemingly remote, find their way back to influence land-management decisions in the redwoods.

A federal tight money policy, for example, lessens the number of new homes that will be built, dropping lumber prices, production, and profits, with varying effects on forest-management plans.

The State Department and the Department of Commerce in recent years have encouraged the export of small, unprocessed logs to Japan and other countries as a means of helping balance the flow of dollars into and out of the United States. Side effects in the western fir and pine regions have been near disastrous. Many lumber mills without an assured supply of logs have been unable to pay inflated prices for their raw material and have had to shut down.

In the redwoods, the Japanese demand for surplus young-growth logs has so far brought more good than harm. Local employment has increased overall, and for the first time the thinning of young stands is economically possible. But the danger of runaway exports will exist as long as the federal government uses logs for ammunition in the world economic battle.

The official doctrine of gradual inflation, the ever-expanding economy concept, has raised the costs of building homes. This tends to hasten development of prefab or unitized methods of construction as a means of cutting on-site labor costs. The effect is already seen in the booming popularity of four-by-eight-foot panels of redwood plywood, while standard redwood lumber sales remain steady. Out in the forest, the policy means that larger logs suitable for peeling are now more valuable.

Government-manipulated fluctuations in the building construction economy have helped establish the myth that the redwood industry is headed for disaster. Proponents of more parks in the region claim that a tourist-based economy therefore is the only salvation. The premise is a faulty one and does nothing to further the cause of either of the industries.

The only source for the basic conclusion is a 1962 study of the area made for the State Office of Planning. With some qualifications, it was predicted that there could be forty percent fewer jobs in the north coast lumber and wood products industry by 1975. This was based on the projected rate of decline in employment per thousand board feet from the years 1958-60, before pulp mills and new plywood mills. But the rate did not continue, and as the target year approaches, the lack of a permanent trend becomes more evident.

Further, that survey defined the North Coast as only three

out of the fifteen redwood counties and added three adjacent inland counties, where the entire timber production is whitewoods. In the redwood industry as a whole, employment has not registered any significant gains or losses in the 1960's nor, with the present land base, is it expected to in the foreseeable future.

"The outlook," concluded the report, "appears to be for a pretty good state of balance over the next 20 years."

The National Park Service study of 1964 limited its definition of the north coast counties to Del Norte, Humboldt, and Mendocino, predicting that they "should enjoy a moderate increase in direct employment in wood products from 17,000 in 1960 to 21,000 in 1980."

The post-World War II housing boom and the Korean War brought heavy demands for lumber. Logging operators and millmen piled into the Redwood Region and boosted production to its all-time high. "A mill sprouted from every stump," they said, "and two from the big ones."

The cut of redwood climbed to the nine-hundred-million-board-foot level for the first time in 1953 and averaged about one billion feet for the next decade, leveling off at nine hundred million in recent years.

The big expansion took place in the production of Douglas-fir lumber. For a number of years, the region put out two billion board feet of whitewood lumber annually. Production has since settled down to a level about equal to that of redwood and is governed largely by the sustained-yield output of the national forests and industrial tree farms.

In 1968, a U.S. Forest Service survey showed the economy of the two national park counties, Del Norte and Humboldt, to be 89.6 percent dependent on timber. Significant, but lesser influence was registered in coastal counties to the south. With redwood, as it always has, claiming a major part of this economic well-being, what is the outlook for the future?

The change-over from an old-growth redwood economy to one largely dependent on regrowth trees poses the biggest challenge for the North Coast. As more producing timberland goes into single-use status—for dams, highways, summer homes, parks, and suburbs—the race becomes closer. The arithmetic shows it can be done, but just barely.

There is an inventory of about twenty-nine billion board feet of redwood in the commercial forests. Half of this is old growth. Some lumber companies will have to switch entirely to young growth in about ten years unless their is some readjustment of supplies. Other firms have enough standing timber to delay the changeover until the twenty-first century.

The transition becomes a matter of the availability of re-growth timber of economic size. The present volume of fifteen billion feet of young timber is expected to rise steadily, according to the National Park Service study, to reach about thirty-one billion by the year 2023. A low point will be reached in the year 1983 when both old- and young-growth supplies will total 27.7 billion feet. At that time, the ratio of growth to cut will be 1.1 and the industry-wide point of sustained yield will be achieved.

Today, supply and demand for redwood products is about in balance. But due to population growth, the nationwide demand for softwood lumber of all species will jump ten percent by 1972, according to the National Forest Products Association. Redwood is not likely to keep pace. For in a trend that puzzles and frightens people of the region, that same wood-using public continues to apply pressures to convert the commercial resource base to other uses, whether it be for wilderness areas or homesites.

At the same time, the remaining land available for forest management is becoming concentrated in stable industrial ownership. The best that can be hoped for in the future is to keep the present acreage of commercial redwoods in a productive condition.

Since the sustained-yield companies will cut timber only as fast as it grows, the redwood supply will be determined almost entirely by the quality of growing sites left in industrial ownership and the intensity of forest management applied to these lands.

Something called the ultra-high-yield forest concept is beginning to claim the attention of industry leaders. Its promise is bright. If we practiced only those management measures we already know how to do, says Miles, we could eventually double the yield of our commercial redwood forests. Examples include the six-year cooperative study on Simpson Timber Company land near Eureka, where it was shown that by adding the woodland equivalent of garden fertilizer, it is possible to grow sixty-year-old-sized redwoods in forty years. A California Polytechnic College researcher has claimed that with today's knowledge and much care, the tallest living redwood could be duplicated within two decades.

All authorities conclude that there are no serious problems or dangers, no threats to the public interest in the management of the commercial redwood forests, and for now at least, they are being handled for what they are—a heritage of many values belonging to us all.

"The lumber companies," says ecologist Raymond F. Dasmann in his book *Destruction of California*, "much maligned though they may be, have been the most conservation-minded, in the broad sense of the word."

The continuing disputes over allocation of the redwoods, then, is not what it is usually pictured to be: of good guys and bad, of preservationists against rapacious timber barons. The drawn-out conflict concerns the question of what constitutes the best kind of conservation.

The great conservation confrontation of our time—the environmental improvers versus the user-exploiters—becomes one of priorities for the allocation of natural resources. And it is in this area that public policy has failed.

Citizens have rarely had the opportunity to vote directly on resource matters. There is no political party of conservation, no straight conservation ticket. The power is held by legislators, organized pressure groups, and government agencies, boards, and commissions. These indirect influences are among the necessary impedimenta of a democracy, and they are for the most part quite responsive to public opinion.

This sensitive area is capable of producing, as we have seen in the redwood national park campaign, the strange spectacle of government agencies, politicians, and conservation pressure groups competing among themselves for a favorable public image.

The circumventing of professional knowledge by public will and whim can be a dangerous game in the light of tomorrow's need for the application of all our hard-won scientific information to the solution of resource shortages, land-use conflicts, and budgeting of the land. The public itself is often the long-run loser in politically motivated resource allocations.

The redwoods, conspicuously at the front of a new wave of environmental upgrading, already offer evidence that professional resource managers are being hindered by a majority of the people who make the laws and influence the policies. Because a majority wants a certain thing does not mean it is right or best. In dealing with nature, a misinformed majority cannot be right.

As Dr. Stone cautions, it is the lay conservationist who may, in the long run, turn out to be the greatest threat to the survival of the superlative redwoods.

In common with the park redwoods, fish and wildlife resources offer another demonstration of how the public is capable of imposing poor management practices, due ironically to the same desire to protect them.

The Bull Creek watershed, entirely within the boundaries of Humboldt Redwoods State Park, developed a large population of deer following earlier logging and forest fires. Since the public does not want hunting in its parks, the basin became a refuge, where the stay-at-home blacktails were protected from hunters. Natural enemies vanished long ago. Herds bulged beyond the carrying capacity of their overused range. With their supply of natural food dwindling, the animals turn to less nourishing sources, including young trees. Meanwhile the roaming animals grind up the topsoil with their sharp hooves, creating future erosion problems. The suffering deer have now declined to a point where the average weight of an adult is about half the normal.

"This range is in danger of being severely damaged—perhaps beyond restoration—if the herd is not thinned each year by hunters," warns the weekly *North Coast Outdoors*. "We feel hunting is a necessity if there is to remain a deer herd at all."

The famous wild elk of Prairie Creek State Park are suddenly faced with a similar fate. Much more than the native deer, they are constant roamers, traveling perhaps twenty miles from home base in the search for food. Before settlement of the area, the five-hundred- to six-hundred-pound wapiti wandered where they pleased, avoiding the dense old-growth forests.

Then as man closed in and the herds reached dangerously low numbers, it was mainly the natural browse food produced by nearby logging that kept the animals alive.

The new Redwood National Park, in combination with the state parks, has placed a biological fence around most of the elks' remaining range. Both logging and periodic hunting seasons authorized by the Fish and Game Commission to prevent over-population and starvation have ended. Sportsmen have lost the last huntable herd of Roosevelt elk in California. The animals must either move on, become an ignoble zoo herd, or suffer the same kind of unnecessary die-offs that periodically hit the elk of Yellowstone National Park.

Nor do fish remain unthreatened by man's interference in the North Coast's outdoor paradise. The dazzling, rare cutthroat trout, reentering their native streams from the ocean, are being crowded out of their spawning beds, warns a Humboldt State College study. The reason? The Department of Fish and Game, responding to the demands of fishermen, has been planting the hardier, more popular salmon and rainbow trout in the cutthroat streams.

Not too far in the future, the migratory salmon and steelhead trout, which made the names of the region's fishing streams sound like music to anglers across the country, will have to face the huge concrete barriers of another public policy, that of the State Water Plan.

Have the redwoods really been saved? There now seems little cause to celebrate the apparent preservation "for all time," as the State Parks Department hopes, of ten percent of the original range in parks and reserves. It has been a magnificent preservation effort, worthy of the stature of the tree. If, as ecologists now suspect, the attempt may have a long-range effect quite the opposite of that intended, the necessary groundwork of those who set this highest conservation example must not be wasted.

If American taxpayers can afford to send men to the moon and spend one hundred million dollars for preservation of the redwoods in a national park, how can we now do less than devote some of our riches to the search for means of perpetuating one of the most beautiful and useful natural resources we found on this earth?

Saving the redwoods now means saving the land that grows them from encroachments, public and private, that hinder the necessary management for perpetuation of the species. It may prove to be the most difficult phase of the continuing conservation battle.

There are the planned reservoirs, for example, that in the north coast area will swallow up about 280,000 acres of land. The state law requiring mitigation for resultant loss of fish and game habitat will take another sixty-four thousand acres. Little of this land is redwood type, but downstream groves may well feel adverse effects.

The first unit of the State Scenic Highway System was established in 1968 and requires natural museum status for one hundred feet of property on either side of the road. If such a "creeping wilderness" pattern were to be applied to roads and park boundaries on one redwood company's property, its forester estimates, thirty percent of the firm's timber would be tied up.

There is no provision so far to compensate private landowners for providing this public benefit, and this brings up one of the stickier problems of the future: payments to landowners whose property rights are confiscated or weakened by scenic easements along wild rivers, riding and hiking trails, parkways, and scenic highways. In redwood country, the cost will be high.

Throughout the state, estimates the University of California, highways, dams, power lines, urban sprawl, and conversion to agriculture are taking two hundred acres of trees every day. In the commercial redwood forests, John Miles fears, the loss to such uses approaches a dozen acres a day.

The state of the art of logging has improved dramatically in the last quarter century, though it remains of concern to some. If further controls are to be written into the Forest Practice Act, they must be based on experience in the field, new knowledge, or the advent of new technologies. The problems of achieving more effective approaches to wise-use conservation, says the Northern California Section of the Society of American Foresters, "are complex ones which cannot be solved by public regulation of management practices." The increased attention paid by the public to the logging of redwoods should not result in laws that are improperly drawn. Good laws serve both our material and aesthetic needs; others can be harmful to both.

Short of human population control, a necessary first step toward rationality in resource management is the adoption of a national land-use policy upon which local and regional policies may be coordinated. The nation's land-using industries are leading a movement in this direction.

Marion Clawson of Resources for the Future suggests a permanent panel of leading citizens, including exploiters and preservationists, to "focus on hard facts, real alternatives and major policies—rather than their reverse, of rumor, fantasy and dreams."

UC's new Public Policy Research Organization has begun a study to "develop organizational means for concentrating diffuse and fragmented authority" on specific problems in the field of natural resources. The Redwood National Park and its continuing difficulties will be a prominent case history.

Ideally, synchronized policies should be followed by planning, allocations, then intensive management, all in the light of future needs.

In the revolution of rising human expectations, coordinated master planning and harmonious management of all our resources is necessary if the limited land area is to provide social and product needs of what seems to be an unlimited future population. Use, development, and preservation of natural resources are potentially compatible with each other. For early proof of this conservation coexistence, there's the faint, pioneering move toward harvesting the total benefits of the forest in the recent adoption of multiple-use principles on both public and private redwood forests.

Restoring the old balance that Edison observed will be difficult, at the least. The Redwood Region is one of America's last forested frontiers, subject to forces that will drastically change its character. If there is a "last-chance" opportunity here, it is to demonstrate whatever we have learned from past mistakes in converting frontiers.

To perpetuate the drama of the redwood, it should be intensely managed for both humanity and natural resources. Something like a total systems approach, embracing informed public policies and enlightened private decisions can provide, as one lumber company's slogan hopefully proclaims, redwoods forever.

No other resource is as deserving of our attention or as full of promise. As the years extend from this 200th anniversary of the gift of our graceful anachronism, man's awesome responsibilities for its future become more pressing. The eternal redwood should wait no longer.

# Selected Bibliography

Black, Peter E. *The Coast Redwoods, Water and Watersheds. A Study for the National Park Service.* Washington, D.C., 1967.

Brown, Alan K. *Sawpits in the Spanish Redwoods.* San Mateo County Historical Society. San Mateo, 1966.

Chaney, Ralph W. *Redwoods of the Past.* Save-the-Redwoods League. San Francisco, 1948.

Clar, C. Raymond. *California Government and Forestry.* California Division of Forestry. Sacramento, 1959.

Cooper, D. W. *The Coast Redwood and Its Ecology.* Agricultural Extension Service, University of California. 1965.

Fritz, Emanuel. *California Coast Redwood. An Annotated Bibliography.* Foundation for American Resource Management. San Francisco, 1957.

————. *Characteristics, Utilization and Management of Second-Growth Redwood.* Foundation for American Research Management. San Francisco, 1959.

————. *The Future of the Redwoods.* Berkeley, 1950.

————. *Properties and Uses of Second Growth Redwood.* California Agricultural Experiment Station. Berkeley, 1923.

————. *Reforestation in Redwood.* University of California School of Forestry. Berkeley, 1949.

Fritz, Emanuel, and Rydelius, James A. *Redwood Reforestation Problems.* Foundation for American Resource Management. Buena Park, California, 1966.

Humboldt State College. *Ecology of the Coast Redwood Region.* Arcata, 1963.

Lewis, Oscar. *The Quest for Qual-A-Wa-Loo.* Privately printed. Eureka, 1943.

Lindquist, James, and Palley, Marshall N. *Empirical Yield Tables for Young-Growth Redwood.* Bulletin 796. California Agricultural Experiment Station, Berkeley.

————. *Prediction of Stand Growth of Young Redwood.* Bulletin 831.

Miles, John Gleason. *The Effect of Commercial Operations on the Future of the Coast Redwood Forest*. National Park Service. 1963.

Nixon, Stuart. *Redwood Empire*. E. P. Dutton & Co. New York, 1966.

Ryder, David Warren. *Memories of the Mendocino Coast*. Privately printed. San Francisco, 1948.

Stranger, Frank M. *Sawmills in the Redwoods*. San Mateo County Historical Association. San Mateo, 1967.

State of California, Department of Parks and Recreation. Sacramento. North Coast Redwood Master Plan. 1965.

State of California, Division of Forestry. Sacramento.
*Relationship of Land Use to 1964-1965 Flood*. 1965.
*Redwood Forest Handbook*. 1948.
*Redwood Sprouts on Jackson State Forest*. Notes No. 29. 1966.

Sunset (magazine) editorial staff. *Redwood Country*. Lane Books. Menlo Park, 1969.

U.S. Forest Service. San Francisco.
*Commercial Forest Area and Timber Volume in California, 1963*. Resource Bulletin PSW-4. 1966.
*Silvical Characteristics of Redwood*. Research Paper PSW-28. 1966.
*Strength and Related Properties of Second-Growth Redwood*. Research Paper FPL-53. 1966.
*The California Coast Redwood—Statistics and Observations on Land Management*. 1964.

University of California. Berkeley.
*A Symposium on Management for Park Preservation*. 1966.
*Commercial Forest Resources and Forest Products Industries*. Agricultural Extension Service. 1965.
*Conference on Young Growth Management*. School of Forestry. 1967.
*Extension Series on California Redwood, 1965-66*. Letters and Science Extension.
*Forestry Seminar Series*. School of Forestry. 1964.

# Useful Pamphlets About the Coast Redwoods

## AMERICAN FOREST INSTITUTE
### 1835 K St. N.W., Washington, D.C. 20006

California Forest Facts

Our Growing Redwoods

## CALIFORNIA DEPARTMENT OF PARKS AND RECREATION
### Resources Building, Sacramento, Calif. 95814

Guides and regulations for each state park (specify by name)

## CALIFORNIA REDWOOD ASSOCIATION
### 617 Montgomery St., San Francisco, Calif. 94111

Redwood Homes

Redwood Industry Recreation Areas

Redwood Interiors

Redwood the Extraordinary

Redwood Vacation Homes

Story of the Redwood Lumber Industry

Story of the Redwood Forest Teachers Kit

The Physiology of the Redwood

The Tall Trees (state park guide)

## NATIONAL PARK SERVICE
### Interior Building, Washington, D.C. 20240

Muir Woods National Monument

Redwood National Park

## REDWOOD EMPIRE ASSOCIATION
### 476 Post St., San Francisco, Calif. 94102

Wayside Folder

Fact Sheets: Aviation, Fishing, Golf, Historical Landmarks

## REDWOOD REGION CONSERVATION COUNCIL
### 224 Rosenberg Building, Santa Rosa, Calif. 95404

Demonstration Forests

Redwood Region Tree Farms

Curriculum Outline for High School Forestry Instruction

## SAVE-THE-REDWOODS LEAGUE
### 114 Sansome St., San Francisco, Calif. 94104

The Story Told by a Fallen Redwood

Trees, Shrubs and Flowers of the Redwood Region

A Living Link in History

## U. S. FOREST SERVICE
### 14th St. & Jefferson Dr., S.W., Washington, D.C. 20250

American Woods—Redwood

Useful Trees #17—Redwood

# Visit a Redwood Mill

Up in the northern end of redwood country, "lumber-watching" has become a diversion attracting more visitors than many state parks. These large mills welcome tens of thousands of tourists each year, some of whom find the spectacle of converting round logs into rectangular lumber so intriguing that they must be reminded when it's closing time.

Some lumber mills shut down for one week during the summer, usually near the first of July. A telephoned inquiry at this period may save disappointment.

Listed from north to south, the following mills are open to visitors during summer months:

CRESCENT CITY (4 miles south)——Miller Redwood Co. Guided tours at 10 A.M. and 2 P.M. weekdays.

- ORICK (2 miles north)——Arcata Redwood Co. Unguided, 7:30 A.M. to 12 noon; 12:30 P.M. to 4 P.M. weekdays.

- ARCATA (3 miles north)——Simpson Timber Co. plywood plant. Guided tours 10 A.M. and 1:30 P.M. weekdays.

- EUREKA (foot of Del Norte St.)——Simpson Timber Co. plywood plant. Guided tours 10 A.M. and 1:30 P.M. weekdays.

SAMOA (across bay from Eureka)——Georgia-Pacific Corp. Guided sawmill tours 2 P.M. weekdays; pulp mill 3 P.M. weekdays. Crown Simpson Pulp Co. guided tours at 11 A.M. and 1 P.M. weekdays.

SCOTIA——The Pacific Lumber Co. Unguided, 7:30 A.M. to 12 noon; 1 P.M. to 4:30 P.M. weekdays.

- FORT BRAGG——Union Lumber Co. Guided tours at 8:30 A.M., 9:30 A.M., 12 noon, 2 P.M. and 4 P.M. weekdays in summer. Balance of year, guided tours at 2 P.M. weekdays.

WILLITS——Willits Redwood Products Co. Unguided, between 10 A.M. and 11 A.M. and 2 P.M. to 4:30 P.M. weekdays. One-day advance notice requested for groups of six or more persons.

# Visit a Demonstration Forest

A pleasant interlude in traveling the major highways of the Redwood Region is a stop at one of the series of living demonstrations of forest management established by the Redwood Region Conservation Council. Here may be seen the amazing regrowth powers of the redwood forest as well as past and present methods of making it more productive. All areas are open to the public without charge during the summer tourist season. Each offers parking space, restrooms, exhibits, and picnic facilities.

**CRESCENT CITY** (4 miles south)——Miller Redwood Co. One half mile east of U.S. 101.

**TRINIDAD** (2 miles north)——Georgia-Pacific Corp. On U.S. 101.

**BLUE LAKE** (2 miles east)——Simpson Timber Co. On U.S. 299.

**SCOTIA** (7 miles south)——The Pacific Lumber Co. On U.S. 101.

**ROCKPORT** (1 mile north)——Georgia-Pacific Corp. On State 1.

**NAVARRO** (1 mile west)——Masonite Corp. On State 128.

# Index